Glencoe

# CHEMISTRY
## MATTER AND CHANGE

# Supplemental Problems

## Glencoe
## McGraw-Hill

New York, New York    Columbus, Ohio    Woodland Hills, California    Peoria, Illinois

A GLENCOE PROGRAM

Glencoe
CHEMISTRY
MATTER AND CHANGE

**Hands-On Learning:**
Laboratory Manual, SE/TE
Forensics Laboratory Manual, SE/TE
CBL Laboratory Manual, SE/TE
Small-Scale Laboratory Manual, SE/TE
ChemLab and MiniLab Worksheets

**Review/Reinforcement:**
Study Guide for Content Mastery, SE/TE
Solving Problems: A Chemistry Handbook
Reviewing Chemistry
Guided Reading Audio Program

**Applications and Enrichment:**
Challenge Problems
Supplemental Problems

**Assessment:**
Chapter Assessment
MindJogger Videoquizzes (VHS/DVD)
Computer Test Bank, Windows/MacIntosh

**Teacher Resources:**
Lesson Plans
Block Scheduling Lesson Plans
Spanish Resources
Section Focus Transparencies and Masters
Math Skills Transparencies and Masters
Teaching Transparencies and Masters
Solutions Manual

**Technology:**
Chemistry Interactive CD-ROM
Vocabulary PuzzleMaker Software,
    Windows/MacIntosh
Glencoe Science Web site:
**science.glencoe.com**

Send all inquiries to:
Glencoe/McGraw-Hill
8787 Orion Place
Columbus, OH 43240-4027

ISBN 0-07-824535-4
Printed in the United States of America.
1 2 3 4 5 6 7 8 9 10 045 09 08 07 06 05 04 03 02 01

# Contents

# To the Teacher

This *Supplemental Problems* book provides additional problems to supplement those in the student edition of ***Chemistry: Matter and Change.*** These problems are provided for each of the chapters for which additional mathematical problems would be beneficial. Most chapters contain 10–25 supplemental problems. You might use them as assessments or assign them for homework. Complete solutions can be found at the back of the *Supplemental Problems* book.

# Data Analysis

**1.** A sample of aluminum is placed in a 25-mL graduated cylinder containing 10.0 mL of water. The level of water rises to 18.0 mL. Aluminum has a density of 2.7 g/mL. Calculate the mass of the sample.

**2.** Saturn is about 1 429 000 km from the Sun. How many meters is Saturn from the Sun? Write your answer in scientific notation.

**3.** Use the graph to answer the questions.

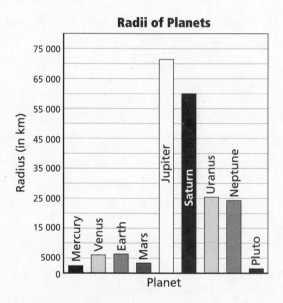

**Radii of Planets**

**a.** What kind of graph is this?

**b.** What are the variables?

**c.** According to the graph, which has a larger radius, Neptune or Uranus?

**d.** According to the graph, what is the radius of Saturn?

**e.** Convert the radius of Saturn to meters. Write your answer in scientific notation.

**4.** Look at the graph below. Then answer the questions.

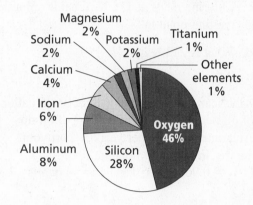

**The Composition of Earth's Crust**

**a.** What kind of graph is this?

**b.** According to the graph, which element is most abundant in Earth's crust?

**c.** According to the graph, what percent of Earth's crust is made up of titanium? Of calcium?

**5.** You place a 28.95-g piece of gold in a 10-mL graduated cylinder. The level of the water rises 1.50 mL. What is the density of gold? You know that silver has a density of 10.5 $g/cm^3$. What mass of silver will raise the level of the water in the graduated cylinder 1.50 mL?

**6.** Convert 55 miles per hour to kilometers per hour. How many kilometers/second is 55 miles per hour? (1 mile = 1.6 km)

**7.** Convert the following data to scientific notation.

**a.** 166 000 000 000 000 $m^2$

**b.** 8847 m

**c.** 484 liters

**8.** Convert the following as indicated.

   **a.** Aluminum boils at 2467°C. What is aluminum's boiling point in kelvins?

   **b.** Bromine melts at −7.2°C. What is bromine's melting point in kelvins?

   **c.** Chlorine melts at 172 K. What is chlorine's melting point in °C?

   **d.** What is 273 K in °C?

**9.** American cars use about 600 000 000 gallons of oil per year. How many liters of oil do American cars use per year? Report your answer in scientific notation.
(1 L = 0.908 quart; 1 gallon = 4 quarts)

**Solve the following problems. Express your answers in proper scientific notation.**

**10. a.** $5.3 \times 10^{12} + 3.0 \times 10^{11} =$

   **b.** $3.7 \times 10^6 - 8.0 \times 10^5 =$

   **c.** $1.85 \times 10^{16} + 9.25 \times 10^{16} =$

   **d.** $2.8 \times 10^{22} + 82 \times 10^{21} =$

   **e.** $3.09 \times 10^{20} - 9.1 \times 10^{19} =$

   **f.** $17 \times 10^3 + 3 \times 10^4 + 1.3 \times 10^4 =$

   **g.** $4.80 \times 10^{15} - 13 \times 10^{13} =$

**11. a.** $(4.0 \times 10^5) \times (3.0 \times 10^3) =$

   **b.** $(5.0 \times 10^{12}) \times (8.05 \times 10^3) =$

   **c.** $(8.9 \times 10^5) \div (3.0 \times 10^3) =$

   **d.** $(1.6 \times 10^{12}) \div (8.01 \times 10^{-3}) =$

   **e.** $(9.0 \times 10^5) \times (3.0 \times 10^{-3}) =$

   **f.** $(2.4 \times 10^3) \div (8.0 \times 10^{-3}) =$

   **g.** $(6.1 \times 10^{-5}) \div (3.01 \times 10^{-2}) =$

**12.** Mac measured the density of silver three times and obtained the following results:

Trial 1: 10.6 g/cm$^3$; Trial 2: 10.8 g/cm$^3$; Trial 3: 9.6 g/cm$^3$.

Silver has a density of 10.5 g/cm$^3$

   **a.** Calculate Mac's percent error for each trial.

   **b.** Which trial had the greatest percent error?

**13.** You calculate that your semester average in history is 97.5. When you get your report card, your average is 96. What was the percent error of your calculation?

**14.** Determine the number of significant figures in each measurement.

   **a.** 0.000 301 5 m

   **b.** 0.121 012 L

   **c.** 1.056 mL

   **d.** 12.90 s

   **e.** 5000 dogs

   **f.** $5.78910 \times 10^3$ g

**15.** Round the number 31.257 592 to the requested number of significant figures.

   **a.** 7 significant figures

   **b.** 5 significant figures

   **c.** 3 significant figures

**16.** Complete the following calculations. Round off the answers to the correct number of significant figures.

   **a.** 2.30 m × 3.65 m × 0.55 m =

   **b.** 103.8 m ÷ 31 s =

   **c.** 26.0 cm × 2.1 cm =

# Matter—Properties and Changes

**1.** An 18-g sample of element A combines completely with a 4-g sample of element B to form the compound AB. What is the mass of the compound formed?

**2.** A substance breaks down into three component elements when it is heated. The mass of each component element is listed in the table below. What was the mass of the substance before it was heated?

| Component | Mass (g) |
|-----------|----------|
| A | 39.10 |
| B | 54.94 |
| C | 64.00 |

**3.** Silver iodide powder has been used as an antiseptic and as an agent to seed clouds for rain. Silver iodide is 45.9% silver by mass. If you separate a 50-g sample of silver iodide into its elements, silver and iodine, how much silver would you have?

**4.** If 5 g of element A combines with 16 g of element B to form compound AB, how many grams of B are needed to form compound $AB_2$? How many grams of B are needed to form $AB_3$?

**5.** During a chemical reaction, 2.445 g of carbon reacts with 3.257 g of oxygen to form carbon monoxide gas. How many grams of carbon monoxide are formed in this reaction?

**6.** Ibuprofen has the chemical formula $C_{13}H_{18}O_2$. It is 75.69% carbon, 8.80% hydrogen, and 15.51% oxygen. How many mg of carbon does a 200-mg tablet of ibuprofen contain?

**7.** During a chemical reaction, 4.032 g of hydrogen combined with oxygen to form 36.032 g of water. How many grams of oxygen reacted?

**8.** Nitrogen and oxygen combine to form different compounds, as shown below.

| Compound | Chemical Formula | Mass N/1 g O |
|----------|------------------|--------------|
| Nitric oxide | NO | 1.76 g |
| Nitrogen dioxide | $NO_2$ | 0.88 g |
| Nitrous oxide | $NO_4$ | 0.44 g |

What is the ratio of the masses of nitrogen in each of the following?

$NO_2/NO_4 = $ _____

$NO/NO_4 = $ _____

$NO/NO_2 = $ _____

**9.** Carbon and oxygen combine to form carbon monoxide (CO) and carbon dioxide ($CO_2$). The masses of oxygen that combine with 12 g of carbon to form these two compounds are 16 g and 32 g, respectively. What is the ratio of the masses of oxygen in $CO_2/CO$?

**10.** Phosphorus and chlorine combine to form two different compounds. In one compound, 3.88 g of phosphorus combines with 13.28 g of chlorine. In the other compound, 1.32 g of phosphorus combines with 7.56 g of chlorine. Do these data support the law of multiple proportions? Show your work.

11. Fluorine and xenon combine to form two different compounds. In one compound, 0.853 g of fluorine combines with 1.472 g of xenon. In the other compound, 0.624 g of fluorine combines with 2.16 g of xenon. Do these data support the law of multiple proportions? Show your work.

12. Ferric chloride is 34.4% iron and 65.6% chlorine by mass. A chemist analyzes three compounds that contain iron and chlorine. Her results are summarized in the data table below. Which of these compounds is likely to be ferric chloride? Explain your answer.

| Compound | Mass of the Sample (g) | Mass of Fe (g) | Mass of Cl (g) |
|---|---|---|---|
| I | 25 | 9.3 | 15.7 |
| II | 25 | 8.6 | 16.4 |
| III | 27 | 9.3 | 17.7 |

13. The chemical formula for baking soda is $NaHCO_3$. A 168.02-g sample of baking soda contains 45.98 g of sodium, 2.02 g of hydrogen, 24.02 g of carbon, and 96 g of oxygen. What is the mass percentage of each element in baking soda?

14. The chemical formula for chalk is $CaCO_3$. A 100-g sample of chalk contains 40 g of calcium, 12 g of carbon, and 48 g of oxygen. What is the mass percentage of each element in chalk? What would be the mass of calcium in 200 g of chalk?

15. A 17-g sample of ammonia, $NH_3$, contains 3 g of hydrogen. What percentage of ammonia is hydrogen? How many grams of nitrogen does the sample contain?

# The Structure of the Atom

**1.** Use the periodic table to complete the following table.

| Element | Atomic Number | Protons | Electrons |
|---|---|---|---|
| **a.** Li | | | |
| **b.** | | | 87 |
| **c.** | 93 | | |
| **d.** Hg | | | 80 |
| **e.** | 81 | | |
| **f.** | 75 | | |
| **g.** B | | | |

**2.** Give the number of protons, electrons, and neutrons in each of the following atoms.

**a.** $^{108}_{47}Au$

**b.** $^{40}_{20}Ca$

**c.** $^{23}_{11}Na$

**3.** Name each isotope, and write it in symbolic notation.

**a.** atomic number 26; mass number 56

**b.** atomic number 29; mass number 64

**c.** atomic number 17; mass number 37

**4.** How many protons, electrons, and neutrons are in each of the following isotopes?

**a.** uranium-235

**b.** hydrogen-3

**c.** silicon-29

**5.** How many neutrons does europium-151 have? What is the isotope's mass number?

**6.** How many more neutrons does thorium-230 have than protons? How many electrons does thorium-230 have?

**7.** Show that the mass number and the number of protons are conserved in the following nuclear equation: $^{234}_{92}U \rightarrow \, ^{230}_{90}Th + \, ^{4}_{2}He$.

**8.** Give the mass number of each isotope.

**a.** Be with 5 neutrons

**b.** Ga with 39 neutrons

**c.** Si with 16 neutrons

**d.** Ti with 26 neutrons

**9.** Give the atomic number of each isotope.

**a.** magnesium-25

**b.** bromine-79

**c.** antimony-121

**10.** Neon has two isotopes: neon-10 and neon-12.

**a.** Which isotope has the greater mass?

**b.** Which has more neutrons?

**c.** Which has more protons?

**d.** Which has more electrons?

**11.** Use the table below to calculate the atomic mass of element *X*. Then use the periodic table to identify the element. Show all your work.

| Isotope | Mass (amu) | Percent Abundance |
|---|---|---|
| $^{16}X$ | 15.995 | 99.762 |
| $^{17}X$ | 16.999 | 0.038 |
| $^{18}X$ | 17.999 | 0.20 |

**12.** Magnesium has three isotopes. Magnesium-24 has a percent abundance of 78.99%. Magnesium-26 has a percent abundance of 11.01%. What is the percent abundance of magnesium-25? Assume that there are no other magnesium isotopes.

**13.** Calculate the atomic mass of iridium. Iridium has two isotopes. Iridium-191 has a mass of 191.0 amu and a percent abundance of 37.58%. Iridium-191 has a mass of 193.0 amu and a percent abundance of 62.42%. Show all your work.

**14.** An element has three naturally occurring isotopes.

Isotope 1 has a mass of 19.992 amu.

Isotope 2 has a mass of 20.994 amu.

Isotope 3 has a mass of 21.991 amu.

The pie graph shows the relative abundance of each isotope.

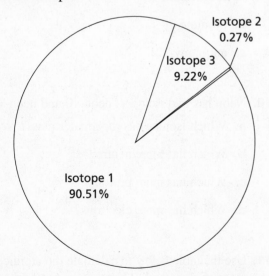

**a.** Calculate the atomic mass of the element.

**b.** Identify the element, using the periodic table.

**15.** An element has three naturally occurring isotopes. Information about each isotope is summarized below.

| Isotope | Mass (amu) | Percent Abundance |
|---------|-----------|-------------------|
| Isotope 1 | 23.985 | 78.10 |
| Isotope 2 | 24.946 | 10.13 |
| Isotope 3 | 25.983 | 11.17 |

**a.** Find the atomic mass of this element. Show all your work.

**b.** Identify the element, using the periodic table.

**c.** Write each isotope in symbolic notation.

**16.** The isotope carbon-14 can be used to determine the ages of objects that were once living, such as wood, bones, and fossils. While alive, living things take in all the isotopes of carbon, including carbon-14. Carbon-14 undergoes radioactive decay continuously. After an organism dies, the carbon-14 in its body continues to decay. However, its body no longer takes in new carbon-14. Thus, by measuring how much carbon-14 a once-living object contains and comparing it with the amount of carbon-14 in a currently living thing, you can determine the age of the object.

**a.** In terms of subatomic structure, how does carbon-14 differ from carbon-12 and carbon-13?

**b.** How is carbon-14 like carbon-12 and carbon-13?

**c.** Carbon-14 emits a beta particle as it decays. What atom does carbon-14 decay to?

**d.** Write an equation to represent the decay of carbon-14.

# Electrons in Atoms

**1.** Orange light has a frequency of $4.8 \times 10^{14}$ s$^{-1}$. What is the energy of one quantum of orange light?

**2.** Which is greater, the energy of one photon of orange light or the energy of one quantum of radiation having a wavelength of $3.36 \times 10^{-9}$m?

**3.** Use the relationships $E = h\nu$ and $c = \lambda v$ to write $E$ in terms of $h$, $c$, and $\lambda$.

**4.** A radio station emits radiation at a wavelength of 2.90 m. What is the station's frequency in megahertz?

**5.** Record the frequency of your favorite radio station. What is the wavelength of the radiation emitted from the station?

**6.** List the sequence in which the following orbitals fill up: 1s, 2s, 3s, 4s, 5s, 6s, 7s, 2p, 3p, 4p, 5p, 6p, 7p, 3d, 4d, 5d, 6d, 4f, 5f.

**7.** Which element has the ground-state electron configuration $[Kr]5s^24d^{10}5p^4$?

**8.** Which element has the ground-state electron configuration $[Ar]4s^23d^{10}$?

**9.** Write electron-dot structures for the following atoms.

**a.** $[Ne]3s^23p^3$

**b.** $[Ar]4s^23d^3$

**c.** potassium

**10.** Complete the following table.

| Element | Symbol | \multicolumn{5}{c}{Orbitals} | Electron Configuration |
|---|---|---|---|---|---|---|---|
| | | 1s | 2s | 2p$_x$ | 2p$_y$ | 2p$_z$ | |
| **a.** Nitrogen | | | | | | | $1s^22s^22p^3$ |
| **b.** | F | ↑↓ | ↑↓ | ↑↓ | ↑↓ | ↑ | |
| **c.** Carbon | | | | | | | |
| **d.** | | | | | | | $1s^22s^1$ |

**11.** Complete the orbital diagram for arsenic.

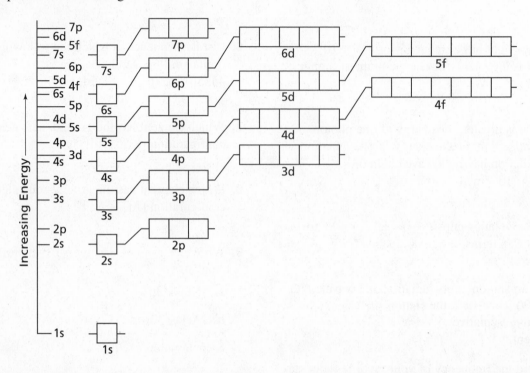

**12.** Use the figure below to answer the following questions.

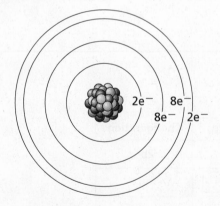

**a.** How many valence electrons does an atom of this element have?

**b.** What is the atom's electron-dot structure?

**c.** If enough energy was added to remove an electron, from which energy level would the electron be removed? Explain your answer.

**13.** What is the ground-state electron configuration of each of the following atoms? Use noble-gas notation.

**a.** selenium

**b.** krypton

**c.** chlorine

**14.** What is the highest energy level (*n*) that is occupied in the following elements?

**a.** He

**b.** Ca

**c.** Sn

**15.** Write the electron configuration for each element described below and identify the element.

**a.** an element that contains 8 electrons

**b.** an element that contains 14 electrons

# The Periodic Table and Periodic Law

**For questions 1–5, do not use the periodic table.**

**1.** Write the electron configurations for the elements in periods 2–4 of group 2A.

**2.** Determine the group, period, and block of the elements with the following electron configurations.

   **a.** $[He]2s^2 2p^4$

   **b.** $[Xe]6s^1$

   **c.** $[Ar]4s^2 3d^{10} 4p^2$

**3.** Categorize each of the elements in problem 2 as a representative element or a transition element.

**4.** Write the electron configuration of the element fitting each of the following descriptions. Use noble-gas notations.

   **a.** Group 8A element in the third period

   **b.** Group 4A element in the fourth period

   **c.** Halogen in the second period

   **d.** Group 1A element in the fourth period

**5.** What are the noble-gas notations of all the elements with the following valence electron configurations?

   **a.** $s^2$

   **b.** $s^2 p^1$

**For questions 6–9, do not use Figure 6-12, 6-15, or 6-20.**

**6.** Rank the following atoms in order of decreasing radii.

   **a.** Al, Na, P, S

   **b.** Al, Ga, In

   **c.** As, Ge, Ga

   **d.** Br, Ca, Cl, K

**7.** Rank the following ions in order of decreasing radii.

   **a.** $Br^-$, $Cl^-$, $F^-$

   **b.** $Be^{2+}$, $Ca^{2+}$, $Mg^{2+}$

   **c.** $Ca^{2+}$, $Ga^{3+}$, $K^+$

**8.** Rank the following particles in order of decreasing radii.

   **a.** I, $I^-$

   **b.** K, $K^+$

   **c.** Al, $Al^{3+}$

**9.** Rank the following atoms in order of decreasing electronegativity.

   **a.** Na, Li, K

   **b.** K, Sc, Ca

   **c.** As, Sn, S

# Chemical Reactions

**Balance the following chemical equations.**

**1.** $SnS_2(s) + O_2(g) \rightarrow SnO_2(s) + SO_2(g)$

**2.** $C_2H_6(g) + O_2(g) \rightarrow CO_2(g) + H_2O(g)$

**3.** $Al(s) + HCl(aq) \rightarrow AlCl_3(aq) + H_2(g)$

**4.** $CoCO_3(s) \rightarrow CoO(s) + CO_2(g)$

**Write a balanced equation for each of the following reactions, substituting symbols and formulas for names. Include the state of each reactant and product. Then identify the reaction type for each. If more than one reaction type applies, list all that apply.**

**5.** When aluminum nitrate and sodium hydroxide solutions are mixed, solid aluminum hydroxide forms. The other product is sodium nitrate.

**6.** When magnesium is heated in the presence of nitrogen gas, solid magnesium nitride forms.

**7.** When solid copper(II) oxide and hydrogen react, metallic copper and water form.

**8.** Most industrial production of metallic sodium is accomplished by passing an electric current through molten sodium chloride. Chlorine gas also is produced.

**9.** Liquid pentane $(C_5H_{12})$ burns, producing water vapor and carbon dioxide.

**10.** When chlorine gas is passed through a potassium bromide solution, bromine forms in a potassium chloride solution.

**11.** Magnesium burns in air to form magnesium oxide.

**Predict the products in each of the following reactions. If no reaction occurs, write *NR*. You may use Figure 10-10 for the relative activities of common metals and halogens.**

**12.** $Rb(s) + CaCl_2(aq)$

**13.** $Pt(s) + MnBr_2(aq)$

**14.** $F_2(g) + NaI(aq)$

**15.** $Zn(s) + AgNO_3(aq)$

**Write a complete ionic equation and a net ionic equation for each of the following double-displacement reactions.**

**16.** $Ba(NO_3)_2(aq) + H_2SO_4(aq) \rightarrow$
$\quad BaSO_4(s) + 2HNO_3(aq)$

**17.** $FeCl_3(aq) + (NH_4)_3PO_4(aq) \rightarrow$
$\quad FePO_4(s) + 3NH_4Cl(aq)$

**18.** $KCl(aq) + AgC_2H_3O_2(aq) \rightarrow$
$\quad AgCl(s) + KC_2H_3O_2(aq)$

# The Mole

1. Identify and calculate the number of representative particles in each of the following quantities.

   a. 2.15 moles of gold

   b. 0.151 mole of nitrogen oxide

   c. 11.5 moles of potassium bromide

2. Calculate the number of moles of the substance that contains the following number of representative particles.

   a. $8.92 \times 10^{23}$ atoms of barium

   b. $5.50 \times 10^{25}$ molecules of carbon monoxide

   c. $2.66 \times 10^{22}$ formula units of potassium iodide

3. Determine the mass in grams of each of the following quantities.

   a. 1.24 moles of beryllium

   b. 3.35 moles of calcium

   c. 0.155 mole of sulfur

4. Calculate the number of moles in each of the following quantities.

   a. 6.35 g lithium

   b. 346 g zinc

   c. 115 g nickel

5. How many atoms are in the following samples?

   a. 1.24 g cobalt

   b. 0.575 g cesium

   c. 65.6 g silicon

6. Which quantity has the greatest mass?

   a. $4.16 \times 10^{23}$ atoms of radium

   b. $1.50 \times 10^{20}$ atoms of cadmium

   c. $1.33 \times 10^{24}$ atoms of argon

7. Calculate the number of moles in each of the following quantities.

   a. atoms of each element in 3.35 moles of aspirin ($C_9H_8O_4$)

   b. positive and negative ions in 1.75 moles of calcium fluoride ($CaF_2$)

8. Determine the molar mass of each of the following compounds.

   a. formic acid ($CH_2O_2$)

   b. ammonium dichromate (($NH_4)_2Cr_2O_7$)

9. What is the mass in grams of each of the following quantities?

   a. 2.53 moles of lead(II) nitrate ($Pb(NO_3)_2$)

   b. 4.62 moles of magnesium bromide ($MgBr_2$)

10. Calculate the number of moles in each of the following samples.

    a. 3.75 g calcium carbide ($CaC_2$)

    b. 245 g aluminum nitrite ($Al(NO_2)_3$)

11. Determine the percent composition of each of the following compounds.

    a. manganese oxide (MnO)

    b. propanol ($C_3H_8O$)

    c. calcium phosphate ($Ca_3(PO_4)_2$)

**12.** Determine the empirical formula for a 100.00-g sample of a compound having the following percent composition.

  **a.** 94.07% sulfur and 5.93% hydrogen

  **b.** 80.68% mercury, 12.87% oxygen, and 6.45% sulfur

**13.** A 48.30-g sample of an aluminum-iodine compound contains 3.20 g of aluminum. What is the empirical formula for the compound?

**14.** A 50.00-g sample of hydrated manganese(II) chloride yields 31.75 g of the anhydrous compound after heating. Determine the chemical formula and name of the hydrate.

**15.** Caffeine is a compound found in some natural coffees and teas and in some colas.

  **a.** Determine the empirical formula for caffeine, using the following composition of a 100.00-g sample.

  49.47 grams of carbon, 28.85 grams of nitrogen, 16.48 grams of oxygen, and 5.20 grams of hydrogen

  **b.** If the molar mass of caffeine is 194.19 g/mol, calculate its molecular formula.

# Stoichiometry

1. Silicon nitride is used in the manufacturing of high-temperature thermal insulation for heat engines and turbines. It is produced by the following reaction.

$$3Si(s) + 2N_2(g) \rightarrow Si_3N_4(s)$$

   a. Interpret the equation in terms of particles, moles, and masses.

   b. Show that mass is conserved in the reaction.

2. The heat from a welder's torch is produced by the burning of acetylene gas. The reaction is represented by the following balanced chemical equation.

$$2C_2H_2(g) + 5O_2(g) \rightarrow 4CO_2(g) + 2H_2O(g)$$

   Calculate the mole ratios from the balanced equation.

3. Limestone ($CaCO_3$) is treated with hydrochloric acid and water to manufacture calcium chloride hexahydrate. This compound is used to melt ice and snow on pavements and roads. The following balanced chemical equation represents the reaction.

$$CaCO_3(s) + 2HCl(aq) + 5H_2O(l) \rightarrow$$
$$CaCl_2 \cdot 6H_2O(s) + CO_2(g)$$

   a. How many moles of calcium chloride hexahydrate will be produced from 4.00 mol calcium carbonate?

   b. How many moles of hydrogen chloride will be needed to produce 1.25 mol of the hydrate?

   c. If 8.33 mol water is available for the reaction, how many moles of carbon dioxide will be released?

4. To prevent corrosion and make paints adhere better, some aluminum products are treated with chromium(III) phosphate before finishing. Chromium(III) phosphate ($CrPO_4$) is commercially produced by treating chromium metal with orthophosphoric acid ($H_3PO_4$).

   a. Balance the following equation for the reaction.

$$\underline{\hspace{1cm}}Cr(s) + \underline{\hspace{1cm}}H_3PO_4(aq) \rightarrow$$
$$\underline{\hspace{1cm}}H_2(g) + \underline{\hspace{1cm}}CrPO_4(s)$$

   b. How many moles of chromium metal are needed to produce 855 g of chromium(III) phosphate?

   c. The reaction of 206 g chromium will release how many moles of hydrogen gas?

5. Sand (silicon dioxide) and coke (carbon) are combined to form silicon carbide (SiC), a compound used in high-strength ceramic materials.

   a. Balance the following equation for the reaction.

$$\underline{\hspace{1cm}}SiO_2(s) + \underline{\hspace{1cm}}C(s) \rightarrow$$
$$\underline{\hspace{1cm}}SiC(s) + \underline{\hspace{1cm}}CO(g)$$

   b. What mass of silicon carbide will be produced from the reaction of 352 g silicon dioxide?

   c. If 1.00 g of carbon is reacted, what mass of carbon monoxide is released?

6. Two compounds of nitrogen, nitrogen tetroxide ($N_2O_4$) and hydrazine ($N_2H_4$), are used as rocket fuels. When the two compounds are mixed, they ignite spontaneously and produce nitrogen gas and water.

   a. Balance the following equation for the reaction.

   _____$N_2O_4(l)$ + _____$N_2H_4(l) \rightarrow$

   _____$N_2(g)$ + _____$H_2O(g)$

   b. If 8.00 g nitrogen tetroxide and 4.00 g hydrazine are mixed, determine the following quantities.

   1. limiting reactant

   2. mass of product ($N_2$)

   3. mass of excess reactant

7. One step in the industrial refining of nickel is the decomposition of nickel carbonyl ($Ni(CO)_4$) into nickel and carbon monoxide. In a laboratory reaction, 25.0 g nickel carbonyl yielded 5.34 g nickel.

   a. Balance the following equation for the reaction.

   _____$Ni(CO)_4(g) \rightarrow$

   _____$Ni(s)$ + _____$CO(g)$

   b. Determine the theoretical yield of nickel.

   c. Determine the percent yield.

# States of Matter

1. Calculate the ratio of effusion rates of oxygen ($O_2$) to hydrogen ($H_2$).

2. Methane ($CH_4$) effuses at a rate of 2.45 mol/s. What will be the effusion rate of argon (Ar) under the same conditions?

3. The effusion rate of hydrogen sulfide ($H_2S$) is 1.50 mol/s. Another gas under similar conditions effuses at a rate of 1.25 mol/s. What is the molar mass of the second gas?

4. The pressure of a gas in a manometer is 12.9 mm Hg. Express this value in each of the following units.

    a. torr

    b. atmosphere

    c. kilopascal

5. The vapor pressure of water is 2.3 kPa at 23°C. What is the vapor pressure of water at this temperature expressed in atmospheres?

6. What is the pressure of a mixture of nitrogen ($N_2$) and oxygen ($O_2$) if the partial pressure of $N_2$ is 594 mm Hg and the partial pressure of $O_2$ is 165 mm Hg?

7. A sample of air is collected at 101.1 kPa. If the partial pressure of water vapor in the sample is 2.8 kPa, what is the partial pressure of the dry air?

8. Suppose that 5-mL containers of helium (He), neon (Ne), and argon (Ar) are at pressures of 1 atm, 2 atm, and 3 atm, respectively. The He and Ne are then added to the container of Ar.

    a. What is the partial pressure of He in the container after the three gases are mixed?

    b. What is the total pressure in the container after the three gases are mixed?

# Gases

1. In one city, a balloon with a volume of 6.0 L is filled with air at 101 kPa pressure. The balloon in then taken to a second city at a much higher altitude. At this second city, atmospheric pressure is only 91 kPa. If the temperature is the same in both places, what will be the new volume of the balloon?

2. A certain mass of gas in a 2.25-L container has a pressure of 164 kPa. What will the new pressure be if the volume of the container is reduced to 1.50 L and the temperature stays constant?

3. If 5.80 dm³ of gas is collected at a pressure of 92.0 kPa, what volume will the same gas occupy at 101.3 kPa if the temperature stays constant?

4. If the volume of an air pump used to inflate a football decreases from 480 mL to 375 mL, and the original pressure was 93.5 kPa, what is the new air pressure in the pump if the temperature stays constant?

5. Maintaining constant pressure, the volume of a gas is increased from 18.0 dm³ to 32.0 dm³ by heating it. If the original temperature was 18.0°C, what is the new temperature in degrees Celsius?

6. A natural gas tank is constructed so that the pressure remains constant. On a hot day when the temperature was 33°C, the volume of gas in the tank was determined to be 3000.0 L. What would the volume be on a warm day when the temperature is 11°C?

7. A 50.0-mL sample of gas is cooled from 119°C to 80.0°C. If the pressure remains constant, what is the final volume of the gas?

8. A 10.0-L cylinder of gas is stored at room temperature (20.0°C) and a pressure of 1800 psi. If the gas is transferred to a 6.0-L cylinder, at what Celsius temperature would it have to be stored in order for the pressure to remain at 1800 psi?

9. If the gas pressure in an aerosol can is 148.5 kPa at 23°C, what is the pressure inside the can if it is heated to 298°C?

10. A tank for compressed gas has a maximum safe pressure limit of 850 kPa. The pressure gauge reads 425 kPa when the temperature is 28°C. What is the highest temperature in degrees Celsius the tank can withstand safely?

11. In a steel container, it was found that the pressure of the gas inside was 160 kPa when the container had been heated to 98°C. What had been the pressure of the gas when the temperature had been 50°C the previous day?

12. A steel cylinder is filled with a gas at a temperature of 25.0°C and a pressure of 225.0 kPa. What will the pressure be if the temperature is raised to 47°C?

13. A balloon is filled with gas at a pressure of 102.3 kPa and a temperature of 45.5°C. Its volume under these conditions is 12.5 L. The balloon is then taken into a decompression chamber where the volume is measured as 2.50 L. If the temperature is 36.0°C, what is the pressure in the chamber?

14. A weather balloon contains 14.0 L of helium at a pressure of 95.5 kPa and a temperature of 12.0°C. If this had been stored in a 1.50-L cylinder at 21.0°C, what must the pressure in the cylinder have been?

15. How many moles of a gas will occupy 2.50 L at STP?

16. Calculate the volume that 3.60 g $H_2$ gas will occupy at STP.

17. What volume is occupied by 0.580 mol of gas at 98.4 kPa and 11°C?

18. When a sample of a gas was placed in a sealed container with a volume of 3.35 L and heated to 105°C, the gas vaporized and the resulting pressure inside the container was 170.0 kPa. How many moles of the gas was present?

19. An engineer wishes to design a container that will hold 14.0 mol of gas at a pressure no greater than 550 kPa and a temperature of 48°C. What is the minimum volume the container can have?

20. What is the molar mass of a sample of gas that has a density of 2.85g/L at 101 kPa pressure and 29°C?

21. How many grams of gas are present in a sample that has a molar mass of 44 g/mol and occupies a 1.8-L container at 108 kPa and 26.7°C?

22. What is the molar mass of a gas if 142 g of the gas occupies a volume of 45.1 L at 28.4°C and 94.6 kPa?

23. Determine the volume of hydrogen gas needed to make 8 L of water vapor.

24. Calculate the volume of chlorine gas at STP that is required to completely react with 3.50 g of silver, using the following equation: $2Ag(s) + Cl_2(g) \rightarrow 2AgCl(s)$.

25. Use the reaction shown to calculate the mass of iron that must be used to obtain 0.500 L of hydrogen at STP.

   $3Fe(s) + 4H_2O(l) \rightarrow Fe_3O_4(s) + 4H_2(g)$

# Solutions

1. The solubility of a gas is 0.34 g/L at STP. What is its solubility at a pressure of 0.80 atm and the same temperature?

2. At 25°C and 1.0 atm, 0.25 g of a gas dissolves in 1.00 L of water. What mass of the gas dissolves in 1.00 L of water at 25°C and 3.0 atm?

3. 1.56 g of a gas dissolves in 2.00 L of water at a pressure of 1.75 atm. At what pressure will 2.00 g of the gas dissolve in 2.00 L of water if the temperature remains constant?

4. What is the percent by mass of 92.3 g of potassium fluoride (KF) dissolved in 1000.0 g of water?

5. A 500.0 g-sample of aqueous hydrogen peroxide ($H_2O_2$) contains 31.50% $H_2O_2$ by mass.
   a. Find the mass of hydrogen peroxide in the solution.
   b. Find the mass of water in the solution.

6. If 24.0 mL of methanol ($CH_3OH$) is dissolved in 48.0 mL of water, determine the percent by volume of methanol in the solution.

7. An aqueous solution of methanol is 45.0% methanol by volume.
   a. Find the volume of methanol in a 250.0-mL sample of the solution.
   b. Find the volume of water in this sample of the solution.

8. What is the molarity of a solution that contains 20.45 g of sodium chloride (NaCl) dissolved in 700.0 mL of solution?

9. Calculate the molarity of 0.205 L of a solution that contains 156.5 g of sucrose ($C_{12}H_{22}O_{11}$).

10. A 0.600-L sample of a 2.50$M$ solution of potassium iodide (KI) contains what mass of KI?

11. What mass of ammonium chloride ($NH_4Cl$) would you use to prepare 85.0 mL of a 1.20$M$ solution $NH_4Cl$?

12. How would you correctly prepare 125 mL of a 0.30$M$ solution of copper(II) sulfate ($CuSO_4$) from a 2.00$M$ solution of $CuSO_4$?

13. A 22.0-mL sample of 12$M$ $H_2SO_4$ is diluted to a volume of 1200.0 mL. What is the molarity of the diluted solution?

14. A mass of 134 g of manganese dibromide ($MnBr_2$) is dissolved in 225 g of water. What is the molality of the solution?

15. Calculate the molality of a solution that contains 106 g naphthalene ($C_{10}H_8$) dissolved in 3.15 mol carbon tetrachloride ($CCl_4$).

16. A solution is made by dissolving 425 g of nitric acid ($HNO_3$) in 535 g of water. Find the mole fraction of nitric acid in the solution.

# Energy and Chemical Change

1. Calculate the amount of heat released in the complete combustion of 8.17 g of Al to form $Al_2O_3(s)$ at 25°C and 1 atm. $\Delta H_f°$ for $Al_2O_3(s)$ = $-1680$ kJ/mol.

$$4Al(s) + 3O_2(g) \rightarrow 2Al_2O_3(s)$$

2. From the following data at 25°C,

$$H_2(g) + Cl_2(g) \rightarrow 2HCl(g) \quad \Delta H = -185 \text{ kJ}$$
$$2H_2(g) + O_2(g) \rightarrow 2H_2O(g) \quad \Delta H = -483.7 \text{ kJ}$$

calculate $\Delta H$ at 25°C for the reaction below.

$$4HCl(g) + O_2(g) \rightarrow 2Cl_2(g) + 2H_2O(g)$$

3. Determine $\Delta S$ for the reaction

$$SO_3(g) + H_2O(l) \rightarrow H_2SO_4(l),$$

given the following entropies.

| Compound | Entropy (J/mol·K) |
|----------|-------------------|
| $SO_3(g)$ | 256.8 |
| $H_2O(l)$ | 70.0 |
| $H_2SO_4(l)$ | 156.9 |

4. Calculate the molar entropy of vaporization for liquid hydrogen iodide at its boiling point, $-34.55$°C.

$$HI(l) \rightleftarrows HI(g) \qquad \Delta H_{vap} = 19.76 \text{ kJ/mol}$$

5. Ozone $(O_3)$ in the atmosphere may react with nitric oxide (NO).

$$O_3(g) + NO(g) \rightarrow NO_2(g) + O_2(g)$$

From the following data, calculate the $\Delta G°$ in kJ for the reaction at 25°C and determine whether the reaction is spontaneous.

$$\Delta H° = -199 \text{ kJ}$$

$$\Delta S° = -4.1 \text{ J/K}$$

6. For the reaction $H_2(g) + S(s) \rightarrow H_2S(g)$, $\Delta H = -20.2$ kJ and $\Delta S = 43.1$ J/K. When will the reaction be spontaneous?

7. The following reaction is nonspontaneous at 25°C.

$$Cu_2O(s) \rightarrow 2Cu(s) + \frac{1}{2}O_2 \text{ (g)}$$

$$\Delta H_f° = 168.6 \text{ kJ}$$

If $\Delta S = 75.8$ J/K, what is the lowest temperature at which the reaction will be spontaneous?

8. Calculate $\Delta H°$ at 25°C for the reaction below.

$$2ZnS(s) + 3O_2(g) \rightarrow 2ZnO(s) + 2SO_2(g)$$
$$\quad -206.0 \qquad 0 \qquad -350.5 \quad -296.8$$
$$\Delta H_f°(\text{kJ/mol})$$

9. How much heat is evolved in the formation of 35.0 g of $Fe_2O_3(s)$ at 25°C and 1.00 atm pressure by the following reaction?

$$4Fe(s) + 3O_2(g) \rightarrow 2Fe_2O_3(s)$$
$$\Delta H_f° \text{ (kJ/mol)} \quad 0 \qquad 0 \qquad -824.2$$

10. Calculate the standard heat of vaporization, $\Delta H_{vap}$, for tin(IV) chloride, $SnCl_4$.
$\Delta H_f° = -511.3$ kJ/mol for $SnCl_4(l)$ and $-471.5$ kJ/mol for $SnCl_4(g)$.

11. Given the following data at 298 K, calculate $\Delta S$ for the given reaction.

$$2Ag_2O(s) \rightarrow 4Ag(s) + O_2(g)$$
$$\Delta S \text{ (J/mol·K)} \quad 121.3 \qquad 42.6 \qquad 205.2$$

**12.** Calculate the $\Delta G°$ at 298 K for the following reaction.

$$Fe_2O_3(s) + 13CO(g) \rightarrow 2Fe(CO)_5(g) + 3CO_2(g)$$
$$\phantom{Fe_2O_3}-824.2 \quad -110.5 \quad\quad -733.8 \quad\quad -393.5$$
$$\Delta H° \text{ (kJ/mol)}$$
$$\phantom{Fe_2O}87.4 \quad\quad 197.6 \quad\quad\quad 445.2 \quad\quad\quad 213.6$$
$$\Delta S° \text{ (J/mol·K)}$$

**13.** Estimate the temperature at which $\Delta G = 0$ for the following reaction.

$$NH_3(g) + HCl(g) \rightarrow NH_4Cl(s)$$
$$\Delta H = -176 \text{ kJ}, \Delta S = -284.5 \text{ J/K}$$

**14.** Consider the reaction below at 25°C for which $\Delta S = 16.1$ J/K.

$$CH_4(g) + N_2(g) + 163.8 \text{ kJ} \rightarrow$$
$$HCN(g) + NH_3(g)$$

At what temperature will this reaction be spontaneous?

**15.** Estimate the temperature above which the following reaction is not spontaneous.

$$PbS(s) + 2HCl(g) \rightarrow PbCl_2(s) + H_2S(g)$$
$$-100.4 \quad -92.31 \quad\quad -359.4 \quad\quad -20.60$$
$$\Delta H_f° \text{ (kJ/mol)}$$
$$-98.70 \quad -95.30 \quad\quad -314.1 \quad\quad -33.60$$
$$\Delta G° \text{ (kJ/mol)}$$

**16.** Copper metal has a specific heat of 0.385 J/g·°C and a melting point of 1083°C. Calculate the amount of heat required to raise the temperature of 22.8 g of copper from 20.0°C to 875°C.

**17.** How many degrees of temperature rise will occur when a 25.0-g block of aluminum absorbs 10.0 kJ of heat? The specific heat of aluminum is 0.897 J/g·°C.

**18.** Find the standard enthalpy of formation for ethylene, $C_2H_4(g)$, given the following data.

$$C_2H_4(g) + 3O_2(g) \rightarrow 2CO_2(g) + 2H_2O(l)$$
$$\Delta H° = -1411 \text{ kJ}$$

$$C(s) + O_2(g) \rightarrow CO_2(g)$$
$$\Delta H° = -393.5 \text{ kJ}$$

$$H_2(g) + \frac{1}{2}O_2(g) \rightarrow H_2O(l)$$
$$\Delta H° = -285.8 \text{ kJ}$$

**19.** Glycine is important for biological energy. The combustion of glycine is given by the following equation.

$$4C_2H_5O_2N(s) + 9O_2(g) \rightarrow$$
$$8CO_2(g) + 10H_2O(l) + 2N_2(g)$$

$$\Delta H = -3857 \text{ kJ}$$

Given that $\Delta H_f°$ $CO_2(g) = -393.5$ kJ/mol and $\Delta H_f°$ $H_2O(l) = -285.8$ kJ/mol, calculate the enthalpy of formation per mole of glycine.

**20.** At body temperature, 2404 J is required to evaporate 1 g of water. After vigorous exercise, a person feels chilly because the body is giving up heat to evaporate the perspiration. A typical person perspires 25 mL of water after 20 minutes of exercise. How much body heat is used to evaporate this water?

# Reaction Rates

**1.** For the reaction $BrO_3^- + 5Br^- + 6H^+ \rightarrow 3Br_2 + 3H_2O$, the value of $\dfrac{-\Delta[BrO_3^-]}{\Delta t} = 1.5 \times 10^{-2}$ mol/(L·s) at a particular time. What is the value of $\dfrac{-\Delta[Br^-]}{\Delta t}$ at the same instant?

**2.** The reaction, $A + 2B \rightarrow$ Products, was found to have the rate law, Rate $= k[A][B]^2$. While holding the concentration of A constant, the concentration of B was increased from $x$ to $3x$. Predict by what factor the rate of the reaction will increase.

**3.** For the hypothetical reaction $A + B \rightarrow$ Products, the following initial rates of reaction have been measured for the given reactant concentrations.

| Test | [A] (M) | [B] (M) | Rate (mol/(L·hr)) |
|------|---------|---------|-------------------|
| 1 | 0.010 | 0.020 | 0.020 |
| 2 | 0.015 | 0.020 | 0.030 |
| 3 | 0.010 | 0.010 | 0.005 |

What is the rate law expression for this reaction?

**4.** For the chemical reaction $H_2O_2 + 2H^+ + 2I^- \rightarrow I_2 + 2H_2O$, the rate law expression is Rate $= k[H_2O_2][I^-]$. The following mechanism has been suggested.

$H_2O_2 + I^- \rightarrow HOI + OH^-$

$OH^- + H+ \rightarrow H_2O$

$HOI + H^+ + I^- \rightarrow I_2 + H_2O$

Identify all intermediates included in this reaction.

**5.** Consider the following rate data for the reaction below at a particular temperature.

$2A + 3B \rightarrow$ Products

| Experiment | Initial [A] (M) | Initial [B] (M) | Initial Rate of Loss of A (mol/(L·s)) |
|------------|-----------------|-----------------|----------------------------------------|
| 1 | 0.10 | 0.30 | $1.00 \times 10^{-5}$ |
| 2 | 0.10 | 0.60 | $2.00 \times 10^{-5}$ |
| 3 | 0.20 | 0.90 | $1.20 \times 10^{-4}$ |

What is the rate equation for this reaction?

**6.** Consider a chemical reaction involving compounds A and B that is found to be first order in A and second order in B. What will the reaction rate be for experiment 2?

| Experiment | Rate (mol/(L·s)) | Initial [A] (M) | Initial [B] (M) |
|------------|------------------|-----------------|-----------------|
| 1 | 0.10 | 1.0 | 0.2 |
| 2 | ? | 2.0 | 0.6 |

**7.** The data below were determined for the following reaction.

$S_2O_8^{2-} + 3I^- \rightarrow 2SO_4^{2-} + I_3$

| Experiment | $[S_2O_8^{2-}]$ (M) | $I^-$ (M) | Initial Rate (mol/(L·s)) |
|------------|---------------------|-----------|--------------------------|
| 1 | 0.10 | 0.40 | $1.4 \times 10^{-5}$ |
| 2 | 0.20 | 0.40 | $2.8 \times 10^{-5}$ |
| 3 | 0.20 | 0.20 | $1.4 \times 10^{-5}$ |

What is the rate equation for this reaction?

**8.** For the reaction A + B → C, the rate relationship is found to be Rate = $k[A][B]^2$. What is the overall reaction order for this reaction?

**9.** For the rate law expression Rate = $k[A][B]^2$, what happens to the rate if the concentration of B is increased by a factor of 2?

**10.** Calculate the specific rate constant for the reaction A + B → C, when the rate expression is Rate = $k[A]^2[B]$.

| Experiment | Initial [A] (*M*) | Initial [B] (*M*) | Initial Rate of Formation of C (mol/(L·s)) |
|---|---|---|---|
| 1 | 0.10 | 0.10 | $2.0 \times 10^{-4}$ |
| 2 | 0.20 | 0.10 | $8.0 \times 10^{-4}$ |
| 3 | 0.20 | 0.20 | $1.6 \times 10^{-3}$ |

**11.** The following figure shows the energy diagram of some reactants changing into products. Explain what the numbers in the diagram represent.

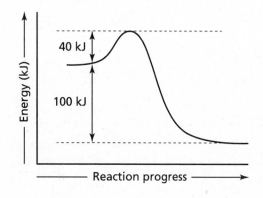

**12.** The following figure shows the potential energy diagram for a reaction. Explain what this diagram tells you about the reaction.

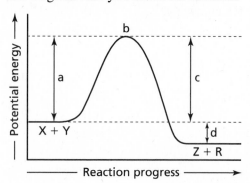

**13.** Explain how the following mechanism can be used to determine the rate expression for a chemical reaction A + 2B → $AB_2$.

| Step 1 | B + B → $B_2$ | slow |
|---|---|---|
| Step 2 | $B_2$ + A → AB + B | fast |
| Step 3 | B + AB → $AB_2$ | fast |

**14.** What is the rate law expression for the following mechanism?

| Step 1 | AB + $C_2$ → $AC_2$ + B | slow |
|---|---|---|
| Step 2 | B + AB → $AB_2$ | fast |
| Step 3 | $AC_2$ + $AB_2$ → $A_2C_2$ + $B_2$ | fast |
| Step 4 | $A_2C_2$ + $B_2$ → $A_2C$ + $B_2C$ | fast |

# Chemical Equilibrium

1. Write equilibrium expressions for the following reactions.

   **a.** $NH_4HS(g) \rightleftharpoons NH_3(g) + H_2S(g)$

   **b.** $4HCl(g) + O_2(g) \rightleftharpoons 2Cl_2(g) + 2H_2O(g)$

   **c.** $PCl_5(g) \rightleftharpoons PCl_3(g) + Cl_2(g)$

   **d.** $CuSO_4 \cdot 3H_2O(s) + 2H_2O(g) \rightleftharpoons$
   $CuSO_4 \cdot 5H_2O(s)$

2. At 793 K, the equilibrium constant for the reaction $NCl_3(g) + Cl_2(g) \rightleftharpoons NCl_5(g)$ is 39.3.

   **a.** Do products or reactants dominate in this equilibrium?

   **b.** If the equilibrium constant for this reaction were less than 1, would the reactants or products be dominant?

3. At 773 K, the reaction $2NO(g) + O_2(g) \rightleftharpoons 2NO_2(g)$ produces the following concentrations: $[NO] = 3.49 \times 10^{-4}M$; $[O_2] = 0.80M$; $[NO_2] = 0.25M$.

   **a.** What is the equilibrium constant expression for the reaction?

   **b.** What is the equilibrium constant for the reaction?

4. If you wished to maximize the products of the following reactions, which concentrations would you lower or raise?

   **a.** $H_2(g) + Br_2(g) \rightleftharpoons 2HBr(g)$

   **b.** $CO_2(g) + H_2(g) \rightleftharpoons CO(g) + H_2O(g)$

   **c.** $SO_2(g) + NO_2(g) \rightleftharpoons SO_3(g) + NO(g)$

   **d.** $C(s) + CO_2(g) \rightleftharpoons 2CO(g)$

5. For each reaction, state whether increasing or decreasing the volume of the reaction vessel would yield more product at equilibrium. Give the reason for your choice.

   **a.** $N_2O_4(g) \rightleftharpoons 2NO_2(g)$

   **b.** $2SO_3(g) \rightleftharpoons 2SO_2(g) + O_2(g)$

   **c.** $CH_4(g) + 2O_2(g) \rightleftharpoons CO_2(g) + 2H_2O(g)$

   **d.** $2CO(g) + O_2(g) \rightleftharpoons 2CO_2(g)$

6. What effect would an increase in temperature have on these reactions at equilibrium? Why?

   **a.** Heat $+ H_2(g) + I_2(g) \rightleftharpoons 2HI(g)$

   **b.** $CH_4(g) + 2O_2(g) \rightleftharpoons CO(g) + 2H_2O + heat$

   **c.** $N_2(g) + 3H_2(g) \rightleftharpoons 2NH_3(g) + heat$

   **d.** Heat $+ CH_4(g) \rightleftharpoons C(s) + 2H_2(g)$

7. Phosphorous pentachloride decomposes to phosphorous trichloride according to this equation: $PCl_5(g) \rightleftharpoons PCl_3(g) + Cl_2(g)$. At equilibrium, $[PCl_5] = 1.00M$ and $[Cl_2] = 3.16 \times 10^{-2}M$.

   **a.** Write the expression for determining the concentration of $PCl_3$.

   **b.** What is the equilibrium concentration of $PCl_3$? Use: $K_{eq} = 1.00 \times 10^{-3}$.

8. The solubility product constant ($K_{sp}$) of $Ag_2SO_4$ is $1.2 \times 10^{-5}$.

   **a.** How would you estimate the molar solubility of $SO_4^{2-}$ without actually calculating it?

   **b.** What is the calculated molar solubility of $SO_4^{2-}$?

# Acids and Bases

**Write balanced chemical equations for each of the following reactions that involve acids and bases.**

1. aluminum and hydrochloric acid

2. nitric acid and sodium carbonate

3. potassium hydroxide and sulfuric acid

**Write the steps in the complete ionization of the following polyprotic acids.**

4. $H_2CO_3$

5. $H_3BO_3$

A solution has a $[H^+]$ of $1.0 \times 10^{-5}M$.

6. What is its $[OH^-]$?

7. What is its pH?

8. What is its pOH?

A solution has a $[OH^-]$ of $3.6 \times 10^{-7}M$.

9. What is its $[H^+]$?

10. What is its pH?

11. What is its pOH?

A solution has a $[H^+]$ of $5.6 \times 10^{-6}M$.

12. What is its $[OH^-]$?

13. What is its pH?

14. What is its pOH?

A solution has a pH of 5.79.

15. What is its pOH?

16. What is its $[H^+]$?

17. What is its $[OH-]$?

18. What is the pH of a $0.50M$ solution of HCl, a strong acid?

19. What is the pH of a $1.5 \times 10^{-3}M$ solution of NaOH, a strong base?

20. What is the molarity of a KOH solution if 25.0 mL of it is neutralized by 31.7 mL of a $0.100M$ nitric acid solution?

21. During a titration, $0.200M$ HCl is added to a NaOH solution of unknown concentration. What is the concentration of the NaOH solution if 20.0 mL of it is neutralized by 30.7 mL of the standard solution?

22. A 25.0-mL sample of $H_2SO_4$ is neutralized by 27.4 mL of $1.00M$ KOH. What is the concentration of the acid?

23. A 50.0-mL sample of $0.0100M$ $Ca(OH)_2$ is neutralized by 45.6 mL of HBr. What is the molarity of the acid?

# Redox Reactions

Determine the oxidation number of the boldface element in these ions.

**1.** $\mathbf{Hg}Cl_4^-$

**2.** $\mathbf{N}O_2$

**3.** $\mathbf{Mn}O_2$

**4.** metallic **Au**

**5.** $Na_2\mathbf{Si}F_6$

**6.** $Zn(\mathbf{N}O_3)_2$

**7.** $Mg_3\mathbf{P}_2$

**8.** $Na_3\mathbf{P}O_4$

**9.** $\mathbf{H}_2O_2$

**10.** $\mathbf{Cl}O_3^-$

Balance the following equations, using the oxidation number method for the redox part of the equation. Show your work.

**11.** $Cu_2O(s) + H_2(g) \rightarrow Cu(s) + H_2O(l)$

**12.** $Cl_2(g) + KBr(aq) \rightarrow Br_2(l) + KCl(aq)$

**13.** $CaSi_2(s) + SbCl_3(s) \rightarrow$
$Sb(s) + Si(s) + CaCl_2(s)$

**14.** $KI(aq) + HNO_3(aq) \rightarrow$
$I_2(s) + KNO_3(aq) + NO(g) + H_2O(l)$

**15.** $Cr_2O_7^{2-}(aq) + SO_3^{2-}(aq) \rightarrow$
$Cr^{3+}(aq) + SO_4^{2-}(aq)$ in an acidic solution

Write half-reactions for each of the following redox reactions. Identify each half-reaction as being either oxidation or reduction.

**16.** $SnS_2(s) + O_2(g) \rightarrow SnO_2(s) + SO_2(g)$

**17.** $Mg(s) + N_2(g) \rightarrow Mg_3N_2(s)$

**18.** $Al(s) + Cl_2(g) \rightarrow AlCl_3(s)$

**19.** $NH_3(aq) + PbO(s) \rightarrow$
$N_2(g) + Pb(s) + H_2O(l)$

**20.** $Cu_2S(s) + O_2(g) \rightarrow Cu^{2+}(aq) + SO_4^{2-}(aq)$
(Hint: Two different elements are oxidized.)

Use your answers for questions 16–20 to help you balance the following equations, using half-reactions for the redox part of the equation. Show your work.

**21.** $SnS_2(s) + O_2(g) \rightarrow SnO_2(s) + SO_2(g)$

**22.** $Mg(s) + N_2(g) \rightarrow Mg_3N_2(s)$

**23.** $Al(s) + Cl_2(g) \rightarrow AlCl_3(s)$

**24.** $NH_3(aq) + PbO(s) \rightarrow N_2(g) + Pb(s) + H_2O(l)$

**25.** $Cu_2S(s) + O_2(g) \rightarrow Cu^{2+}(aq) + SO_4^{2-}(aq)$ in an acidic solution (Hint: Look at the ratio of the two oxidized elements in the equation.)

# Electrochemistry

Use data from Table 21-1 as needed in the following problems. Assume that all half-cells are under standard conditions.

**1.** For each of these pairs of half-reactions, write a balanced equation for the overall cell reaction and calculate the standard cell potential, $E^0_{cell}$.

**a.** $Cs^+(aq) + e^- \rightarrow Cs(s)$

$Cu^+(aq) + e^- \rightarrow Cu(s)$

Cell reaction:

$E^0_{cell} =$

**b.** $Hg^{2+}(aq) + 2e^- \rightarrow Hg(l)$

$Mn^{2+}(aq) + 2e^- \rightarrow Mn(s)$

Cell reaction:

$E^0_{cell} =$

**c.** $Fe^{3+}(aq) + 3e^- \rightarrow Fe(s)$

$Cr^{3+}(aq) + 3e^- \rightarrow Cr(s)$

Cell reaction:

$E^0_{cell} =$

**d.** $Br_2(g) + 2e^- \rightarrow 2Br^-(aq)$

$Au^+(aq) + e^- \rightarrow Au(s)$

Cell reaction:

$E^0_{cell} =$

**e.** $Be^{2+}(aq) + 2e^- \rightarrow Be(s)$

$Tl^{3+}(aq) + 3e^- \rightarrow Tl(s)$

Cell reaction:

$E^0_{cell} =$

**f.** $NO_3^-(aq) + 4H^+(aq) + 3e^- \rightarrow$
$NO(g) + 2H_2O(l)$

$In^{3+}(aq) + 3e^- \rightarrow In(s)$

Cell reaction:

$E^0_{cell} =$

**g.** $H_3PO_4(aq) + 2H^+(aq) + 2e^- \rightarrow$
$H_3PO_3(aq) + H_2O(l)$

$SeO_4^{2-}(aq) + 4H^+(aq) + 2e^- \rightarrow$
$H_2SeO_3(aq) + H_2O(l)$

Cell reaction:

$E^0_{cell} =$

**h.** $MnO_4^-(aq) + 8H^+(aq) + 5e^- \rightarrow$
$Mn^{2+}(aq) + 4H_2O(l)$

$2CO_2(g) + 2H^+(aq) + 2e^- \rightarrow H_2C_2O_4(aq)$

Cell reaction:

$E^0_{cell} =$

**2.** Calculate the standard cell potential, $E^0_{cell}$, for a cell composed of a $Sn|Sn^{2+}$ half-cell and each of these half-cells.

**a.** $Pd|Pd^{2+}$

$E^0_{cell} =$

**b.** $Hf|Hf^{4+}$

$E^0_{cell} =$

**c.** $Cl_2|Cl^-$

$E^0_{cell} =$

**d.** $Pb|Pb^{2+}$

$E^0_{cell} =$

**3.** Which of the following cells will produce the highest voltage?

$Mn|Mn^{2+}\|Zn^{2+}|Zn$

$Zn|Zn^{2+}\|Ni^{2+}|Ni$

$Ni|Ni^{2+}\|Cu^{2+}|Cu$

**4.** For each of these overall cell reactions, write the oxidation and reduction half-reactions, calculate the standard cell potential, $E^0_{cell}$, and determine if the reaction is spontaneous or not.

**a.** $Fe^{3+}(aq) + Co^{2+}(aq) \rightarrow$
   $Fe^{2+}(aq) + Co^{3+}(aq)$

   Oxidation half-reaction:

   Reduction half-reaction:

   $E^0_{cell} =$

   Spontaneous?

**b.** $Fe^{3+}(aq) + Cu^+(aq) \rightarrow$
   $Fe^{2+}(aq) + Cu^{2+}(aq)$

   Oxidation half-reaction:

   Reduction half-reaction:

   $E^0_{cell} =$

   Spontaneous?

**c.** $3Ni^{2+}(aq) + 2Rh(s) \rightarrow$
   $3Ni(s) + 2Rh^{3+}(aq)$

   Oxidation half-reaction:

   Reduction half-reaction:

   $E^0_{cell} =$

   Spontaneous?

**d.** $2Na^+(aq) + 2Hg(l) + 2I^-(aq)$
   $\rightarrow 2Na(s) + Hg_2I_2(s)$

   Oxidation half-reaction:

   Reduction half-reaction:

   $E^0_{cell} =$

   Spontaneous?

**e.** $O_2(g) + 2H_2SO_3(aq) \rightarrow$
   $2SO_4^{2-}(aq) + 4H^+(aq)$

   Oxidation half-reaction:

   Reduction half-reaction:

   $E^0_{cell} =$

   Spontaneous?

**5.** Suppose a battery-powered device requires a minimum voltage of 9.0 V to run. How many lead–acid cells would be needed to run the device? (Remember that a standard automobile battery contains six lead–acid cells connected in one package.) The overall reaction of a lead–acid cell is

$Pb(s) + PbO_2(s) + 4H^+(aq) + 2SO_4^{2-}(aq)$
   $\rightarrow 2PbSO_4(s) + 2H_2O(l)$

**6.** What is the minimum voltage that must be applied to a Down's cell to cause the electrolysis of molten sodium chloride? The net cell reaction is

$2Na^+(l) + 2Cl^-(l) \rightarrow 2Na(l) + Cl_2(g)$

**7.** One way to determine the metallic composition of an alloy is to use electroplating. Suppose an electrolytic cell is set up with solution of nickel ions obtained from a 6.753-g sample of a nickel alloy. The cell also contains a platinum electrode that has a mass of 10.533 g. Electric current is used to reduce the nickel ions to nickel metal, which is deposited on the platinum electrode. After being plated with nickel, the platinum electrode has a mass of 15.042 g. What is the percentage of nickel in the alloy?

# Hydrocarbons

**1.** Use the IUPAC rules to name the following alkanes.

 **a.** $CH_3CH_2CH_2CH_2CH_3$

 **b.**
$$CH_3CHCHCH_3$$
 with $CH_3$ above the second carbon and $CH_3$ below the third carbon

 **c.**
 $CH_3CH_2CHCHCHCH_2CH_3$ with $CH_3$ and $CH_2CH_3$ above, and $CH_2CH_3$ below

 **d.**
 $CH_3CH_2$ ... $CH_2CH_3$ with $CH_3$ at top, $CH_3$ and $CH_3$ on ring, and $CH_2CH_3$ at bottom

**2.** Draw the structure of each of the following alkanes.

 **a.** 4-propyloctane

 **b.** 3,4-diethylhexane

 **c.** 2,2,4,4-tetramethylhexane

 **d.** 1-ethyl-3-methyl-2-propylcyclopentane

**3.** Calculate the number of hydrogen atoms in each of the following alkanes.

 **a.** heptane

 **b.** cyclooctane

**4.** Calculate the molecular mass of a 22-carbon branched-chain alkane.

**5.** Chemists can analyze the composition of hydrocarbons by reacting them with copper oxide. The reaction converts carbon into carbon dioxide and hydrogen into water. Suppose 29 g of a hydrocarbon reacts to produce 88 g of $CO_2$ and 45 g of $H_2O$.

 **a.** What are the masses of carbon and hydrogen in the hydrocarbon?

 **b.** What is the empirical formula of the hydrocarbon?

 **c.** If the hydrocarbon's molecular mass is 58 amu, what is its molecular formula?

**6.** Carbon has an electronegativity of 2.5. Hydrogen has an electronegativity of 2.2. Use these values to decide whether each of the following bonds is polar or nonpolar.

 **a.** C-C

 **b.** C-H

 **c.** H-H

**7.** The combustion of a saturated hydrocarbon releases 657 kJ per mole of $-CH_2-$ groups and 779 kJ per mole of $-CH_3$ groups in the hydrocarbon. How much energy is released by the combustion of 1.00 L of liquid tetradecane (molecular formula $C_{14}H_{30}$), a major component of kerosene? The density of tetradecane is 0.764 g/mL.

**8.** Use the IUPAC rules to name the following hydrocarbons.

**a.** $CH_3CH_2CH{=}CHCH_3$

**b.**
$$CH{=}CH_2$$
$$CH_3CH_2CH_2CHCH_2CH_2CH_2CH_3$$

**c.**
$$CH_3$$
$$CH_3CHCH_2CH_2C{\equiv}CH$$

**d.** $CH_3$
      $CH_2CH_3$

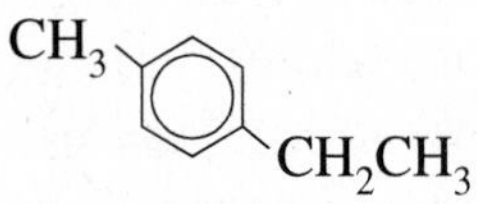

**9.** Draw the structure of each of the following hydrocarbons.

**a.** 7-methyl-2,5-nonadiene

**b.** 4-ethyl-2-heptyne

**c.** 1,2-diethylcyclohexene

**d.** 1-ethyl-2-methyl-5-propylbenzene

**10.** Calculate the number of hydrogen atoms in each of the following unsaturated hydrocarbons.

**a.** 2-pentene

**b.** 1-hexyne

**11.** Write a balanced equation for the reaction in which calcium carbide, $CaC_2$, reacts with water to form ethyne and calcium hydroxide.

# The Chemistry of Life

1. Calculate the molecular masses of the following biological molecules.

   a. Lysine, $NH_2(CH_2)_4CHNH_2COOH$

   b. Fructose, $CH_2OHCO(CHOH)_3CH_2OH$

   c. Oleic acid,
      $CH_3(CH_2)_7CH=CH(CH_2)_7COOH$

2. Write a balanced equation for the condensation reaction in which cysteine and glycine combine to form a dipeptide. Assume the carboxyl group of cysteine reacts.

   cysteine          glycine

3. In a peptide or protein that contains $n$ amino acids, the number of possible amino acid sequences is $A^n$, where $A$ is the number of different amino acids.

   a. How many amino acid sequences are possible for a polypeptide that contains 10 amino acids?

   b. How many different dipeptides can be made from the amino acids leucine (Leu) and valine (Val)? What are those dipeptides?

4. Write a balanced equation for the condensation reaction in which lauric acid, palmitic acid, and stearic acid combine with glycerol to form a triglyceride.

   $CH_3(CH_2)_{10}COOH$    $CH_3(CH_2)_{14}COOH$
       lauric acid               palmitic acid

           $CH_3(CH_2)_{16}COOH$
              stearic acid

5. In saponification, the ester bonds of a triglyceride are hydrolyzed by a strong base, such as NaOH. It takes 3 moles of NaOH to saponify each mole of triglyceride. How many moles of triglyceride can be saponified by 120 g of NaOH?

6. A young adult male produces about $2.4 \times 10^{-5}$ mol per day of the steroid sex hormone testosterone. The molecular mass of testosterone is 288. How many grams of testosterone per day does a young adult male produce?

7. Synthesizing fats is an efficient way for organisms to store energy. The catabolism of 1 g of fat yields about 38 kJ of energy, whereas the catabolism of 1 g of protein or carbohydrate yields about 17 kJ of energy.

   a. How much carbohydrate would be needed to store the same amount of energy as 10 g of fat?

   b. A cup (133 g) of ice cream contains about 32 g of carbohydrate, 4.8 g of protein, and 14 g of fat. How much energy is released when a cup of ice cream is fully catabolized?

   c. A person expends about 840 kJ per hour while walking at a moderate pace. How long would a person have to walk to expend all of the energy contained in a cup of ice cream?

8. A scientist analyzes a sample of DNA and finds that 21% of the nucleotide bases are A and 29% of the bases are C. What percentage of the bases are T and what percentage are G in the sample?

**9.** It takes three consecutive nucleotides in a DNA molecule to code for one amino acid in a protein. If a single strand of DNA contains 747 nucleotides, how many amino acids would be in the protein that it codes for?

**10.** The DNA in a bacterial cell contains about $4.2 \times 10^6$ complementary base pairs. Each base pair has an average length of $3.4 \times 10^{-10}$ m. How long is the DNA in a bacterial cell? Assume that the DNA is stretched out straight rather than coiled.

**11.** One mole of ATP stores approximately 30.5 kJ of energy. This energy is released when ATP is hydrolyzed.

    **a.** Approximately 38 moles of ATP is produced for each mole of glucose that is catabolized in cellular respiration. How much energy is stored in ATP when 5.0 moles of glucose is catabolized in cellular respiration?

    **b.** Assume that 40% of this energy can be used to drive anabolic reactions when ATP is hydrolyzed. The rest will be lost as heat. How much energy will be lost as heat if all of the ATP produced in part a is hydrolyzed?

**12.** A scientist performed an experiment to monitor photosynthesis by a plant. In the experiment, the plant produced 61 g of glucose.

    **a.** How many moles of glucose did the plant produce?

    **b.** How many moles of $O_2$ did the plant produce?

    **c.** How many moles of $CO_2$ were needed to produce that much glucose?

    **d.** What mass of water was needed to produce that much glucose?

**13.** An average-sized woman produces about 1900 g of carbon dioxide per day.

    **a.** How many moles of glucose must be oxidized during cellular respiration to produce that much carbon dioxide?

    **b.** How much energy would be stored in ATP when that much glucose is oxidized?

**14.** Suppose the catabolism of a given amount of glucose produces 95 moles of ATP during cellular respiration. How many moles of ATP could be produced by the same amount of glucose during fermentation?

**15.** How many grams of glucose are needed to produce 102 g of ethanol during alcoholic fermentation?

**16.** Write a balanced equation for lactic acid fermentation. The formula for lactic acid is $CH_3CH(OH)COOH$.

# Nuclear Chemistry

**Write a complete nuclear equation for each of the following.**

**1.** The decay of $^{53}_{26}$Fe by beta emission.

**2.** The decay of $^{230}_{90}$Th by alpha emission.

**3.** The decay of $^{37}_{18}$Ar by electron capture.

**4.** The decay of $^{38}_{19}$K by positron emission.

**5.** The decay of $^{93}_{43}$Tc by gamma emission.

**Provide the missing term in each of the following equations.**

**6.** $^{11}_{5}$B $+ \, ^{4}_{2}$He $\rightarrow \, ^{14}_{7}$N $+$ _____

**7.** $^{45}_{20}$Ca $+ \, ^{1}_{1}$p $\rightarrow \, ^{45}_{21}$Sc $+$ _____

**8.** $^{15}_{7}$N $+$ _____ $\rightarrow \, ^{18}_{8}$O $+ \, ^{1}_{1}$p

**9.** $^{233}_{92}$U $+ \, ^{1}_{0}$n $\rightarrow \, ^{99}_{42}$Mo $+ \, 3^{1}_{0}$n $+$ _____

**10.** _____ $\rightarrow \, ^{206}_{82}$Pb $+ \, ^{4}_{2}$He

**11.** $^{142}_{58}$Ce $+$ _____ $\rightarrow \, ^{142}_{59}$Pr $+ \, ^{1}_{0}$n

**12.** $^{102}_{44}$Ru $+ \, ^{4}_{2}$He $\rightarrow \, ^{1}_{0}$n $+$ _____

**Answer the following questions about half-life.**

**13.** The half-life of $^{115}_{51}$Sb is 32 minutes. How much of a 16.0-g sample of this isotope will remain at the end of 3.0 hours?

**14.** The half-life of $^{182}_{72}$Hf is $9.0 \times 10^6$ years. How much of a 1.0-g sample of this isotope will remain at the end of 40.0 million years?

**15.** The isotope strontium-90 is produced during the testing of nuclear weapons. If 100.0 mg of strontium-90 was released in the atmosphere in 1960, how much of the radioisotope remains 85 years later? The half life of strontium-90 is 29 years.

**16.** The radioisotope technetium-99 is often used as a radiotracer to detect disorders of the body. It has a half-life of 6.01 hours. If a patient received a 25.0-mg dose of this isotope during a medical procedure, how much would remain 48.0 hours after the dose was given?

# SUPPLEMENTAL PROBLEMS
## Answer Key

# Chapter 2

**1.** A sample of aluminum is placed in a 25-mL graduated cylinder containing 10.0 mL of water. The level of water rises to 18.0 mL. Aluminum has a density of 2.7 g/mL. Calculate the mass of the sample.

22 g

Solution:
Volume = 18.0 mL − 10.0 mL = 8.0 mL

mass = volume × density
= 8.0 mL × 2.7 g/mL = 22 g

**2.** Saturn is about 1 429 000 km from the Sun. How many meters is Saturn from the Sun? Write your answer in scientific notation.

$1.429 \times 10^9$ m

Solution:
1 429 000 × 1000 m/1 km = 1 429 000 000 m
= $1.429 \times 10^9$ m

**3.** Look at the graph below. Then answer the questions.

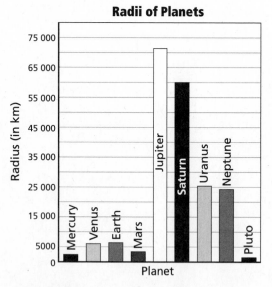

**Radii of Planets**

**a.** What kind of graph is this?

bar graph

**b.** What are the variables shown?

planet name and planet radius

**c.** According to the graph, which has a larger radius, Neptune or Uranus?

Uranus

**d.** According to the graph, what is the radius of Saturn?

60 000 km

**e.** Convert the radius of Saturn to meters. Write your answer in scientific notation.

$6 \times 10^7$ m

Solution:
60 000 km × 1000 m/1 km = 60 000 000 m
= $6 \times 10^7$ m

**4.** Look at the graph below. Then answer the questions.

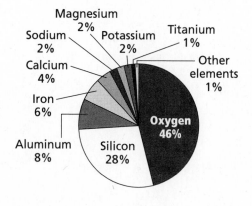

**The Composition of Earth's Crust**

**a.** What kind of graph is this?

circle graph

**b.** According to the graph, which element is most abundant in Earth's crust?

oxygen

**c.** According to the graph, what percent of Earth's crust is made up of titanium? Of calcium?

1% titanium; 4% calcium

**5.** You place a 28.95-g piece of gold in a 10-mL graduated cylinder. The level of the water rises 1.50 mL. What is the density of gold? You know that silver has a density of 10.5 g/cm$^3$. What mass of silver will raise the level of the water in the graduated cylinder 1.50 mL?

19.3 g/mL; 15.8 g

Solution:

density = $\frac{mass}{volume}$ = 28.95 g/1.50 mL = 19.3 g/mL

mass = volume × density = 1.50 mL × 10.5 g/mL

= 15.75 g = 15.8 g

**6.** Convert 55 miles per hour to kilometers per hour. How many kilometers/second is 55 miles per hour? (Use: 1 mile = 1.6 km)

88 km/h; 0.024 km/s

Solution:

(55 mi/h) × (1.6 km /1 mi) = 88 km/h

(88 km/h) × (1 h/60 min) × (1 min/60 s)
= 0.024 km/s or 2.4 × 10$^{-2}$ km/s

**7.** Convert the following data to scientific notation.

**a.** 166 000 000 000 000 m$^2$

1.66 × 10$^{14}$ m$^2$

**b.** 8847 m

8.847 × 10$^3$ m

**c.** 484 liters

4.84 × 10$^2$ liters

**8.** Convert the following as indicated.

**a.** Aluminum boils at 2467°C. What is aluminum's boiling point in SI units?

The SI unit of temperature is kelvin.

Temperature in degrees Celsius (°C) + 273
= temperature in kelvins (K)

2467°C + 273 = 2740 K

**b.** Bromine melts at −7.2°C. What is bromine's melting point in kelvins?

Temperature in degrees Celsius (°C) + 273
= temperature in kelvins (K)

−7.2°C + 273 = 266 K

**c.** Chlorine melts at 172 K. What is chlorine's melting point in °C?

Temperature in kelvins (K) − 273
= temperature in degrees Celsius (°C)

172 K − 273 = −100.98°C

**d.** What is 273 K in °C?

Temperature in kelvins (K) − 273
= temperature in degrees Celsius (°C)

273 − 273 = 0°C

**9.** American cars use about 600 000 000 gallons of oil per year. How many liters of oil do American cars use per year? Report your answer in scientific notation.
(1 liter = 0.908 quart; 1 gallon = 4 quarts)

3 × 10$^9$ L

Solution:
(600 000 000 gallons) × (4 quarts/1 gallon) ×
(1 L/0.908 quart) = 2 643 171 806 L = 3 × 10$^9$ L

**Solve the following problems. Express your answers in proper scientific notation.**

**10. a.** 5.3 × 10$^{12}$ + 3.0 × 10$^{11}$ =

5.6 × 10$^{12}$

**b.** $3.7 \times 10^6 - 8.0 \times 10^5 =$

$2.9 \times 10^6$

**c.** $1.85 \times 10^{16} + 9.25 \times 10^{16} =$

$1.11 \times 10^{17}$

**d.** $2.8 \times 10^{22} + 82 \times 10^{21} =$

$1.1 \times 10^{23}$

**e.** $3.09 \times 10^{20} - 9.1 \times 10^{19} =$

$2.18 \times 10^{20}$

**f.** $17 \times 10^3 + 3 \times 10^4 + 1.3 \times 10^4 =$

$6 \times 10^4$

**g.** $4.80 \times 10^{15} - 13 \times 10^{13} =$

$4.67 \times 10^{15}$

Solution:
One way to solve each problem is shown below.
Students may choose to solve the problems
differently.

a. $5.3 \times 10^{12} + 3.0 \times 10^{11} = 5.3 \times 10^{12} +$
   $0.3 \times 10^{12} = 5.6 \times 10^{12}$

b. $3.7 \times 10^6 - 8.0 \times 10^5 = 3.7 \times 10^6 -$
   $0.8 \times 10^6 = 2.9 \times 10^6$

c. $1.85 \times 10^{16} + 9.25 \times 10^{16} = 11.1 \times 10^{16} =$
   $1.11 \times 10^{17}$

d. $2.8 \times 10^{22} + 8.2 \times 10^{21} = 2.8 \times 10^{22} +$
   $8.2 \times 10^{22} = 11 \times 10^{22} = 1.1 \times 10^{23}$

e. $3.09 \times 10^{20} - 9.1 \times 10^{19} = 3.09 \times 10^{20} -$
   $0.91 \times 10^{20} = 2.18 \times 10^{20}$

f. $17 \times 10^3 + 3 \times 10^4 + 1.3 \times 10^4 = 1.7 \times 10^4$
   $+ 3 \times 10^4 + 1.3 \times 10^4 = 6 \times 10^4$

g. $4.80 \times 10^{15} - 13 \times 10^{13} = 4.80 \times 10^{15} - 0.13$
   $\times 10^{15} = 4.67 \times 10^{15}$

**11. a.** $(4.0 \times 10^5) \times (3.0 \times 10^3) =$

$1.2 \times 10^9$

**b.** $(5.0 \times 10^{12}) \times (8.05 \times 10^3) =$

$4.0 \times 10^{16}$

**c.** $(8.9 \times 10^5) \div (3.0 \times 10^3) =$

$3.0 \times 10^2$

**d.** $(1.6 \times 10^{12}) \div (8.01 \times 10^{-3}) =$

$2.0 \times 10^{14}$

**e.** $(9.0 \times 10^5) \times (3.0 \times 10^{-3}) =$

$2.7 \times 10^3$

**f.** $(2.4 \times 10^3) \div (8.0 \times 10^{-3}) =$

$3.0 \times 10^5$

**g.** $(6.1 \times 10^{-5}) \div (3.01 \times 10^{-2}) =$

$2.0 \times 10^{-3}$

Solution:
One way to solve each problem is shown below.
Students may choose to solve the problems
differently.

a. $(4.0 \times 10^5) \times (3.0 \times 10^3) = 12 \times 10^8 =$
   $1.2 \times 10^9$

b. $(5.0 \times 10^{12}) \times (8.05 \times 10^3) = 40.25 \times 10^{15} =$
   $4.0 \times 10^{16}$

c. $(8.9 \times 10^5) \div (3.0 \times 10^3) = 2.96 \times 10^2 =$
   $3.0 \times 10^2$

d. $(1.6 \times 10^{12}) \div (8.01 \times 10^{-3}) = 0.2 \times 10^{15} =$
   $2.0 \times 10^{14}$

e. $(9.0 \times 10^5) \times (3.0 \times 10^{-3}) = 27 \times 10^2 =$
   $2.7 \times 10^3$

f. $(2.4 \times 10^3) \div (8.0 \times 10^{-3}) = 0.3 \times 10^6 =$
   $3.0 \times 10^5$

g. $(6.1 \times 10^{-5}) \div (3.0 \times 10^{-2}) = 2.03 \times 10^{-3} =$
   $2.0 \times 10^{-3}$

**12.** Mac measured the density of silver three times
and obtained the following results:

Trial 1: 10.6 g/cm$^3$; Trial 2: 10.8 g/cm$^3$;
Trial 3: 9.6 g/cm$^3$.

Silver has a density of 10.5 g/cm$^3$

**a.** Calculate Mac's percent error for each trial.

Trial 1: 0.95%; Trial 2: 2.86%; Trial 3: 8.6%

**b.** Which trial had the greatest percent error?

Trial 3

Solution:

a.  percent error = $\dfrac{\text{error}}{\text{accepted value}} \times 100\%$

Trial 1: percent error =

$\dfrac{(10.6 \text{ g/cm}^3 - 10.5 \text{ g/cm}^3)}{10.5 \text{ g/cm}^3} \times 100\% = 0.952\%$

Trial 2: percent error =

$\dfrac{(10.8 \text{ g/cm}^3 - 10.5 \text{ g/cm}^3)}{10.5 \text{ g/cm}^3} \times 100\% = 2.86\%$

Trial 3: percent error =

$\dfrac{(9.6 \text{ g/cm}^3 - 10.5 \text{ g/cm}^3)}{10.5 \text{ g/cm}^3} \times 100\% = 8.6\%$

**13.** You calculate that your semester average in history is 97.5. When you get your report card, your average is 96. What was the percent error of your calculation?

1.6%

Solution:

percent error = $\dfrac{\text{error}}{\text{accepted value}} \times 100\%$

percent error = $\dfrac{97.5 - 96}{96} \times 100\%$

= 1.5625% = 1.6%

**14.** Determine the number of significant figures in each measurement.

**a.** 0.000 301 5 m

4

**b.** 0.121 012 L

6

**c.** 1.056 mL

4

**d.** 12.90 s

4

**e.** 5000 dogs

infinite, or unlimited

**f.** 5.78910 × 10$^3$ g

6

**15.** Round the number 31.257 592 to the requested number of significant figures.

**a.** 7 significant figures

31.257 59

**b.** 5 significant figures

31.258

**c.** 3 significant figures

31.3

**16.** Complete the following calculations. Round off the answers to the correct number of significant figures.

**a.** 2.30 m × 3.65 m × 0.55 m =

4.62 m$^3$

**b.** 103.8 m ÷ 31 s =

3.3 m/s

**c.** 26.0 cm × 2.1 cm =

55 cm$^2$

# Chapter 3

**1.** An 18-g sample of element A combines completely with a 4-g sample of element B to form the compound AB. What is the mass of the compound formed?

$Mass_{reactants} = Mass_{products}$

$Mass_A + Mass_B = Mass_{AB}$

$Mass_{AB} = 18\ g + 4\ g = 22\ g$

**2.** A substance breaks down into three component elements when it is heated. The mass of each component element is listed in the table below. What was the mass of the substance before it was heated?

| Component | Mass (g) |
|-----------|----------|
| A | 39.10 |
| B | 54.94 |
| C | 64.00 |

$Mass_{reactants} = Mass_{products} = 39.10 + 54.94 + 64.00 = 158.04\ g$

**3.** Silver iodide powder has been used as an antiseptic and as an agent to seed clouds for rain. Silver iodide is 45.9% silver by mass. If you separate a 50-g sample of silver iodide into its elements, silver and iodine, how much silver would you have?

From the conservation of mass, the mass of silver recovered is equal to the mass of silver in the initial silver iodide sample. The amount of silver recovered would be 50.0 g × 45.9% = 50.0 × 0.459 = 22.95 g = 23 g.

**4.** If 5 g of element A combines with 16 g of element B to form compound AB, how many grams of B are needed to form compound AB$_2$? How many grams of B are needed to form AB$_3$?

Compound AB$_2$ contains twice as much element B as does compound AB. Therefore, 2 × 6 g = 32 g.

There is 32 g of B in AB$_2$. Compound AB$_3$ contains three times as much element B as does compound AB. Therefore, 3 × 16 g = 48 g. There is 48 g of B in AB$_3$.

**5.** During a chemical reaction, 2.445 g of carbon reacts with 3.257 g of oxygen to form carbon monoxide gas. How many grams of carbon monoxide are formed in this reaction?

$Mass_{reactants} = Mass_{products}$

$Mass_{carbon} + Mass_{oxygen} = Mass_{carbon\ monoxide}$

$2.445\ g + 3.257\ g = 5.702\ g$

**6.** Ibuprofen has the chemical formula $C_{13}H_{18}O_2$. It is 75.69% carbon, 8.80% hydrogen, and 15.51% oxygen. How many mg of carbon does a 200-mg tablet of ibuprofen contain?

Mass percentage of an element (%) =

$$\frac{Mass\ of\ element}{Mass\ of\ compound} \times 100\%$$

$$Mass\ percentage_{carbon} = \frac{Mass_{carbon}}{Mass_{compound}} \times 100\%$$

$$75.69\%\ carbon = \frac{Mass_{carbon}}{200\ mg} \times 100\%$$

$$75.69\%\ carbon \times \frac{200\ mg}{100\%} = Mass_{carbon}$$

$Mass_{carbon}$ in the tablet = 151.38 mg

**7.** During a chemical reaction, 4.032 g of hydrogen combined with oxygen to form 36.032 g of water. How many grams of oxygen reacted?

$Mass_{reactants} = Mass_{products}$

$Mass_{hydrogen} + Mass_{oxygen} = Mass_{water}$

$4.032\ g + Mass_{oxygen} = 36.032\ g$

$Mass_{oxygen} = 36.032\ g - 4.032\ g = 32\ g$

**8.** Nitrogen and oxygen combine to form different compounds, as shown below.

| Compound | Chemical Formula | Mass N/1 g O |
|---|---|---|
| Nitric oxide | NO | 1.76 g |
| Nitrogen dioxide | $NO_2$ | 0.88 g |
| Nitrous oxide | $NO_4$ | 0.44 g |

What is the ratio of the masses of nitrogen in each of the following?

$NO_2/NO_4$ = _____

$$\frac{0.88 \text{ g}}{0.44 \text{ g}} = 2$$

$NO/NO_4$ = _____

$$\frac{1.76 \text{ g}}{0.44 \text{ g}} = 4$$

$NO/NO_2$ = _____

$$\frac{1.76 \text{ g}}{0.88 \text{ g}} = 2$$

**9.** Carbon and oxygen combine to form carbon monoxide (CO) and carbon dioxide ($CO_2$). The masses of oxygen that combine with 12 g of carbon to form these two compounds are 16 g and 32 g, respectively. What is the ratio of the masses of oxygen in $CO_2/CO$?

$$\frac{\text{Mass ratio}_{\text{carbon dioxide}}}{\text{Mass ratio}_{\text{carbon monoxide}}} = \frac{32 \text{ g}}{16 \text{ g}} = 2$$

**10.** Phosphorus and chlorine combine to form two different compounds. In one compound, 3.88 g of phosphorus combines with 13.28 g of chlorine. In the other compound, 1.32 g of phosphorus combines with 7.56 g of chlorine. Do these data support the law of multiple proportions? Show your work.

First, find the mass ratio for each compound.

Compound I: $\dfrac{\text{Mass}_P}{\text{Mass}_{Cl}} = \dfrac{3.88 \text{ g}}{13.28 \text{ g}} = 0.292$

Compound II: $\dfrac{\text{Mass}_P}{\text{Mass}_{Cl}} = \dfrac{1.32 \text{ g}}{7.56 \text{ g}} = 0.175$

Then, compare the two mass ratios.

$$\frac{\text{Mass ratio}_{\text{compound I}}}{\text{Mass ratio}_{\text{compound II}}} = \frac{0.292}{0.175} = 1.67$$

These data are not consistent with the law of multiple proportions. The law of multiple proportions states that the different masses of Y that combine with a fixed mass of X can be expressed as a ratio of small whole numbers, and 1.67 is not a whole number.

**11.** Fluorine and xenon combine to form two different compounds. In one compound, 0.853 g of fluorine combines with 1.472 g of xenon. In the other compound, 0.624 g of fluorine combines with 2.16 g of xenon. Do these data support the law of multiple proportions? Show your work.

First, find the mass ratio for each compound.

Compound I: $\dfrac{\text{Mass}_F}{\text{Mass}_{Xe}} = \dfrac{0.853 \text{ g}}{1.472 \text{ g}} = 0.579$

Compound II: $\dfrac{\text{Mass}_F}{\text{Mass}_{Xe}} = \dfrac{0.624 \text{ g}}{2.16 \text{ g}} = 0.289$

Then, compare the two mass ratios.

$$\frac{\text{Mass ratio}_{\text{compound I}}}{\text{Mass ratio}_{\text{compound II}}} = \frac{0.579}{0.289} = 2.00$$

These data are consistent with the law of multiple proportions. The law of multiple proportions states that the different masses of Y that combine with a fixed mass of X can be expressed as a ratio of small whole numbers, and 2 is a whole number.

**12.** Ferric chloride is 34.4% iron and 65.6% chlorine by mass. A chemist analyzes three compounds that contain iron and chlorine. Her results are summarized in the data table below. Which of these compounds is likely to be ferric chloride? Explain your answer.

| Compound | Mass of the Sample (g) | Mass of Fe (g) | Mass of Cl (g) |
|---|---|---|---|
| I | 25 | 9.3 | 15.7 |
| II | 25 | 8.6 | 16.4 |
| III | 27 | 9.3 | 17.7 |

First, find the percent of iron by mass in each compound.

$$\text{Mass percentage}_{iron} = \frac{\text{Mass}_{iron}}{\text{Mass}_{compound\ I}} \times 100\%$$

$$= \frac{9.3\ g}{25\ g} \times 100\% =$$

37.2%

$$\text{Mass percentage}_{iron} = \frac{\text{Mass}_{iron}}{\text{Mass}_{compound\ II}} \times 100\%$$

$$= \frac{8.6\ g}{25\ g} \times 100\% = 34.4\%$$

$$\text{Mass percentage}_{iron} = \frac{\text{Mass}_{iron}}{\text{Mass}_{compound\ III}} \times 100\%$$

$$= \frac{9.3\ g}{27\ g} \times 100\% = 34.4\%$$

Then, find the percent of chlorine by mass in each compound.

$$\text{Mass percentage}_{chlorine} = \frac{\text{Mass}_{chlorine}}{\text{Mass}_{compound\ I}} \times 100\%$$

$$= \frac{15.7\ g}{25\ g} \times 100\% = 62.8\%$$

$$\text{Mass percentage}_{chlorine} = \frac{\text{Mass}_{chlorine}}{\text{Mass}_{compound\ II}} \times 100\%$$

$$= \frac{16.4\ g}{25\ g} \times 100\% = 65.6\%$$

$$\text{Mass percentage}_{chlorine} = \frac{\text{Mass}_{chlorine}}{\text{Mass}_{compound\ III}} \times 100\%$$

$$= \frac{17.7\ g}{27\ g} \times 100\% = 65.6\%$$

Compounds II and III have the same composition as ferric chloride.

**13.** The chemical formula for baking soda is $NaHCO_3$. A 168.02-g sample of baking soda contains 45.98 g of sodium, 2.02 g of hydrogen, 24.02 g of carbon, and 96 g of oxygen. What is the mass percentage of each element in baking soda?

$$\text{Mass percentage}_{sodium} = \frac{\text{Mass}_{sodium}}{\text{Mass}_{baking\ soda}} \times 100\%$$

$$= \frac{45.98\ g}{168.02\ g} \times 100\% = 27.36\%$$

$$\text{Mass percentage}_{hydrogen} = \frac{\text{Mass}_{hydrogen}}{\text{Mass}_{baking\ soda}} \times 100\%$$

$$= \frac{2.02\ g}{168.02\ g} \times 100\% = 1.20\%$$

$$\text{Mass percentage}_{carbon} = \frac{\text{Mass}_{carbon}}{\text{Mass}_{baking\ soda}} \times 100\%$$

$$= \frac{24.02\ g}{168.02\ g} \times 100\% = 14.30\%$$

$$\text{Mass percentage}_{oxygen} = \frac{\text{Mass}_{oxygen}}{\text{Mass}_{baking\ soda}} \times 100\%$$

$$= \frac{96\ g}{168.02\ g} \times 100\% = 57.14\%$$

**14.** The chemical formula for chalk is $CaCO_3$. A 100-g sample of chalk contains 40 g of calcium, 12 g of carbon, and 48 g of oxygen. What is the mass percentage of each element in chalk? What would be the mass of calcium in 200 g of chalk?

$$\text{Mass percentage}_{calcium} = \frac{\text{Mass}_{calcium}}{\text{Mass}_{chalk}} \times 100\%$$

$$= \frac{40\ g}{100\ g} \times 100\% = 40\%$$

$$\text{Mass percentage}_{carbon} = \frac{\text{Mass}_{carbon}}{\text{Mass}_{chalk}} \times 100\%$$

$$= \frac{12\ g}{100\ g} \times 100\% = 12\%$$

$$\text{Mass percentage}_{oxygen} = \frac{\text{Mass}_{oxygen}}{\text{Mass}_{chalk}} \times 100\%$$

$$= \frac{48\ g}{100\ g} \times 100\% = 48\%$$

$$\text{Mass percentage}_{calcium} = \frac{\text{Mass}_{calcium}}{\text{Mass}_{chalk}} \times 100\%$$

$$\text{Mass}_{calcium} = \frac{(40\%)(200\ g)}{100\%} = 80\ g$$

**15.** A 17-g sample of ammonia, $NH_3$, contains 3 g of hydrogen. What percentage of ammonia is hydrogen? How many grams of nitrogen does the sample contain?

$$\text{Mass percentage}_{hydrogen} = \frac{\text{Mass}_{hydrogen}}{\text{Mass}_{ammonia}} \times 100\%$$

$$= \frac{3\ g}{17\ g} \times 100\% = 18\%$$

$Mass_{reactants} = Mass_{products}$

$Mass_{nitrogen} + Mass_{hydrogen} = Mass_{ammonia}$

$Mass_{nitrogen} = Mass_{ammonia} - Mass_{hydrogen}$

$14\ g = 17\ g - 3\ g$

# Chapter 4

**1.** Use the periodic table to complete the following table.

Atomic number = number of protons = number of electrons

| Element | Atomic Number | Protons | Electrons |
|---------|---------------|---------|-----------|
| **a.** Li | 3 | 3 | 3 |
| **b.** Fr | 87 | 87 | 87 |
| **c.** Np | 93 | 93 | 93 |
| **d.** Hg | 80 | 80 | 80 |
| **e.** Tl | 81 | 81 | 81 |
| **f.** Re | 75 | 75 | 75 |
| **g.** B | 5 | 5 | 5 |

**2.** Give the number of protons, electrons, and neutrons in each of the following atoms.

Atomic number = number of protons = number of electrons

Number of neutrons = mass number − atomic number

**a.** $^{108}_{47}Au$

47 protons, 47 electrons, 61 neutrons
(108 − 47 = 61)

**b.** $^{40}_{20}Ca$

20 protons, 20 electrons, 20 neutrons
(40 − 20 = 20)

**c.** $^{23}_{11}Na$

11 protons, 11 electrons, 12 neutrons
(23 − 11 = 12)

**3.** Name each isotope, and write it in symbolic notation.

**a.** atomic number 26; mass number 56

iron-56; $^{56}_{26}Fe$

**b.** atomic number 29; mass number 64

copper-64; $^{64}_{29}Cu$

**c.** atomic number 17; mass number 37

chlorine-37; $^{37}_{17}Cl$

**4.** How many protons, electrons, and neutrons are in each of the following isotopes?

Atomic number = number of protons − number of electrons

Number of neutrons = mass number − atomic number

**a.** uranium-235

92 protons, 92 electrons, 143 neutrons
(235 − 92 = 143)

**b.** hydrogen-3

1 proton, 1 electron, 2 neutrons
(3 − 1 = 2)

**c.** silicon-29

14 protons, 14 electrons, 15 neutrons
(29 − 14 = 15)

**5.** How many neutrons does europium-151 have? What is the isotope's mass number?

Number of neutrons = mass number − atomic number

= 151 − 63 = 88 neutrons

The mass number is 151.

**6.** How many more neutrons does thorium-230 have than protons? How many electrons does thorium-230 have?

Number of neutrons = mass number − atomic number

= 230 − 90 = 140 neutrons

Difference between the number of protons and the number of neutrons = 140 − 90 = 50

Therefore, thorium-230 has 50 more neutrons than it does protons.

Atomic number = number of protons = number of electrons

Therefore, thorium-230 has 90 electrons.

**7.** Show that the mass number and the number of protons are conserved in the following nuclear equation: $^{234}_{92}U \rightarrow ^{230}_{90}Th + ^{4}_{2}He$.

Nuclear equation: $^{234}_{92}U \rightarrow ^{230}_{90}Th + ^{4}_{2}He$

Mass number: 234 → 230 + 4

Atomic number: 92 → 90 + 2

**8.** Give the mass number of each isotope.

Number of neutrons + number of protons = mass number

**a.** Be with 5 neutrons

5 neutrons + 4 protons = 9

**b.** Ga with 39 neutrons

39 neutrons + 31 protons = 70

**c.** Si with 16 neutrons

16 neutrons + 14 protons = 30

**d.** Ti with 26 neutrons

26 neutrons + 22 protons = 48

**9.** Give the atomic number of each isotope.

From the periodic table,

**a.** magnesium-25

12

**b.** bromine-79

35

**c.** antimony-121

51

**10.** Neon has two isotopes: neon-10 and neon-12.

**a.** Which isotope has the greater mass?

neon-12

**b.** Which has more neutrons?

neon-12

**c.** Which has more protons?

They have an equal number of protons.

**d.** Which has more electrons?

They have an equal number of electrons.

**11.** Use the table below to calculate the atomic mass of element *X*. Then use the periodic table to identify the element. Show all your work.

| Isotope | Mass (amu) | Percent Abundance |
|---|---|---|
| $^{16}X$ | 15.995 | 99.762 |
| $^{17}X$ | 16.999 | 0.038 |
| $^{18}X$ | 17.999 | 0.20 |

Mass contribution = (mass)(percent abundance)

$^{16}X$: (15.995 amu)(99.762%) = 15.957 amu

$^{17}X$: (16.999 amu)(0.038%) = 0.0065 amu

$^{18}X$: (17.999 amu)(0.20%) = 0.036 amu

Atomic mass of $X$ = 15.957 amu + 0.0065 amu + 0.036 amu = 16.000 amu

The element is oxygen.

**12.** Magnesium has three isotopes. Magnesium-24 has a percent abundance of 78.99%. Magnesium-26 has a percent abundance of 11.01%. What is the percent abundance of magnesium-25? Assume that there are no other magnesium isotopes.

All the percentages should add up to 100%. Therefore:

100% = (percent abundance of magnesium-24) + (percent abundance of magnesium-25) + (percent abundance of magnesium-26)

100% = 78.99% + (percent abundance of magnesium-25) + 11.01%

Percent abundance of magnesium-25 = 100% − (78.99% + 11.01%) = 10.00%

**13.** Calculate the atomic mass of iridium. Iridium has two isotopes. Iridium-191 has a mass of 191.0 amu and a percent abundance of 37.58%. Iridium-191 has a mass of 193.0 amu and a percent abundance of 62.42%. Show all your work.

Mass contribution = (mass)(percent abundance)

Ir-191: (191.0 amu)(37.58%) = 71.78 amu

Ir-193: (193.0 amu)(62.42%) = 120.5 amu

Atomic mass of Ir = 71.78 amu + 120.5 amu = 192.3 amu

**14.** An element has three naturally occurring isotopes.

Isotope 1 has a mass of 19.992 amu.

Isotope 2 has a mass of 20.994 amu.

Isotope 3 has a mass of 21.991 amu.

The pie graph shows the relative abundance of each isotope.

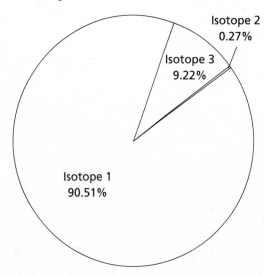

**a.** Calculate the atomic mass of the element.

Mass contribution = (mass)(percent abundance)

Isotope 1: (19.992 amu)(90.51%) = 18.10 amu

Isotope 2: (20.994 amu)(0.27%) = 0.057 amu

Isotope 3: (21.991 amu)(9.22%) = 2.03 amu

Atomic mass = 18.10 amu + 0.057 amu + 2.03 amu = 20.19 amu

**b.** Identify the element, using the periodic table.

The element is neon.

**15.** An element has three naturally occurring isotopes. Information about each isotope is summarized below.

| Isotope | Mass (amu) | Percent Abundance |
|---------|-----------|-------------------|
| Isotope 1 | 23.985 | 78.10 |
| Isotope 2 | 24.946 | 10.13 |
| Isotope 3 | 25.983 | 11.17 |

**a.** Find the atomic mass of this element. Show all your work.

Mass contribution = (mass)(percent abundance)

Isotope 1: (23.985 amu)(78.70%) = 18.88 amu

Isotope 2: (24.946 amu)(10.13%) = 2.531 amu

Isotope 3: (25.983 amu)(11.17%) = 2.902 amu

Atomic mass of element = 18.88 amu + 2.527 amu + 2.902 amu = 24.31 amu

**b.** Identify the element, using the periodic table.

The element is magnesium.

**c.** Write each isotope in symbolic notation.

$^{24}_{12}$Mg, $^{25}_{12}$Mg, $^{26}_{12}$Mg

**16.** The isotope carbon-14 can be used to deter-mine the ages of objects that were once living, such as wood, bones, and fossils. While alive, living things take in all the isotopes of carbon, including carbon-14. Carbon-14 undergoes radioactive decay continuously. After an organ-ism dies, the carbon-14 in its body continues to decay. However, its body no longer takes in new carbon-14. Thus, by measuring how much carbon-14 a once-living object contains and comparing it with the amount of carbon-14 in a currently living thing, you can determine the age of the object.

**a.** In terms of subatomic structure, how does carbon-14 differ from carbon-12 and carbon-13?

Carbon-14 has 8 neutrons, carbon-12 has 6 neutrons, and carbon-13 has 7 neutrons. Carbon-14 has a larger atomic mass than the other two isotopes have.

**b.** How is carbon-14 like carbon-12 and carbon-13?

All three isotopes have 6 protons and 6 elec-trons. They all show the same physical and chemical properties of the element carbon.

**c.** Carbon-14 emits a beta particle as it decays. What atom does carbon-14 decay to?

If carbon-14 emits a beta particle, then it must become nitrogen-14 ($-1 + x = 6$; thus, $x = 7$, which is the atomic number of nitrogen).

**d.** Write an equation to represent the decay of carbon-14.

The equation that shows this change is $^{14}_{6}$C $\rightarrow$ $^{14}_{7}$N + $^{0}_{-1}\beta$.

# Chapter 5

**1.** Orange light has a frequency of $4.8 \times 10^{14}$ s$^{-1}$. What is the energy of one quantum of orange light?

$E_{photon} = h\nu = (6.626 \times 10^{-34}$ J$\cdot$s$)(4.8 \times 10^{14}$ s$^{-1})$
$= 3.18048 \times 10^{-19}$ J $= 3.2 \times 10^{-19}$ J

**2.** Which is greater, the energy of one photon of orange light or the energy of one quantum of radiation having a wavelength of $3.36 \times 10^{-9}$m?

Calculate the frequency: $c = \lambda\nu$,

therefore, $\nu = \dfrac{c}{\lambda}$

$\nu = (3.00 \times 10^8$ m/s$)/(3.36 \times 10^{-9}$ m$)$
$= 8.93 \times 10^{16}$ s$^{-1}$

Calculate the energy of one quantum:
$E_{photon} = h\nu$

$E_{photon} = (6.626 \times 10^{-34}$ J$\cdot$s$)(8.93 \times 10^{16}$ s$^{-1})$
$= 5.92 \times 10^{-17}$ J

From problem 1, orange light has an energy of $3.2 \times 10^{-19}$ J. Therefore, a quantum of radiation with a wavelength of $3.36 \times 10^{-9}$ m has more energy than orange light does.

**3.** Use the relationships $E = h\nu$ and $c = \lambda\nu$ to write $E$ in terms of $h$, $c$, and $\lambda$.

From $c = \lambda\nu$, $\nu = \dfrac{c}{\lambda}$.

$E = h\nu = \dfrac{hc}{\lambda}$

**4.** A radio station emits radiation at a wavelength of 2.90 m. What is the station's frequency in megahertz?

$c = \lambda v$, therefore, $v = \dfrac{c}{\lambda}$

$v = \dfrac{3.00 \times 10^8 \, \cancel{m}/s}{2.90 \, \cancel{m}} = 1.034 \times 10^8 \, s^{-1}$

$1.034 \times 10^{-8} \, s^{-1} = 103.4 \times 10^{-6} \, s^{-1}$
$= 103.4$ megahertz

You can tune in at 103.4 FM.

**5.** Record the frequency of your favorite radio station. What is the wavelength of the radiation emitted from the station?

Answers will vary. Students should use $c = \lambda v$, where $c = 3.00 \times 10^8$ m/s, to calculate the wavelength of their favorite radio station.

**6.** List the sequence in which the following orbitals fill up: 1s, 2s, 3s, 4s, 5s, 6s, 7s, 2p, 3p, 4p, 5p, 6p, 7p, 3d, 4d, 5d, 6d, 4f, 5f.

The correct order is as follows:
1s, 2s, 2p, 3s, 3p, 4s, 3d, 4p, 5s, 4d, 5p, 6s, 4f, 5d, 6p, 7s, 5f, 6d, 7p

**7.** Which element has the ground-state electron configuration $[Kr]5s^2 4d^{10} 5p^4$?

tellurium

**8.** Which element has the ground-state electron configuration $[Ar]4s^2 3d^{10}$?

zinc

**9.** Write electron-dot structures for the following atoms.

**a.** $[Ne]3s^2 3p^3$

$\cdot \overset{\displaystyle ..}{\underset{\displaystyle .}{P}} \cdot$

**b.** $[Ar]4s^2 3d^3$

$\cdot V \cdot$

**c.** potassium

$K \cdot$

**10.** Complete the following table.

| Element | Symbol | Orbitals | | | | | Electron Configuration |
|---|---|---|---|---|---|---|---|
| | | 1s | 2s | 2p$_x$ | 2p$_y$ | 2p$_z$ | |
| **a.** Nitrogen | N | ↑↓ | ↑↓ | ↑ | ↑ | ↑ | $1s^2 2s^2 2p^3$ |
| **b.** Fluorine | F | ↑↓ | ↑↓ | ↑↓ | ↑↓ | ↑ | $1s^2 2s^2 2p^5$ |
| **c.** Carbon | C | ↑↓ | ↑↓ | ↑ | ↑ | | $1s^2 2s^2 2p^2$ |
| **d.** Lithium | Li | ↑↓ | ↑ | | | | $1s^2 2s^1$ |

**11.** Complete the orbital diagram for arsenic.

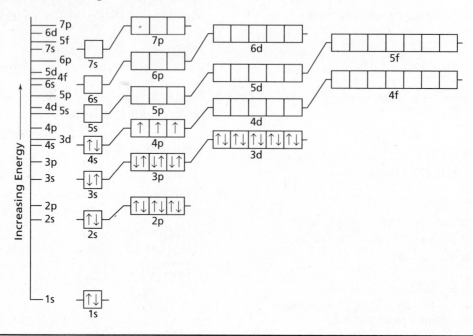

**12.** Use the figure below to answer the following questions.

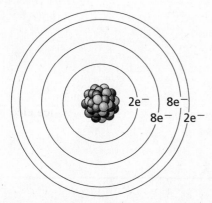

**a.** How many valence electrons does an atom of this element have?

2

**b.** What is the atom's electron-dot structure?

•Ca•

**c.** If enough energy was added to remove an electron, from which energy level would the electron be removed? Explain your answer.

The first electron to leave the atom would be one in the highest energy level, which is the fourth energy level. Electrons in the highest energy level are the least attracted to the nucleus because they are the most distant.

**13.** What is the ground-state electron configuration of each of the following atoms? Use noble-gas notation.

**a.** selenium

$[Ar]4s^23d^{10}4p^4$

**b.** krypton

$[Kr]$ or $[Ar]4s^23d^{10}4p^6$

**c.** chlorine

$[Ne]3s^23p^5$

**14.** What is the highest energy level ($n$) that is occupied in the following elements?

**a.** He

$n = 1$

**b.** Ca

$n = 4$

**c.** Sn

$n = 5$

**15.** Write the electron configuration for each element described below and identify the element.

**a.** an element that contains 8 electrons

$1s^2 2s^2 2p^4$

**b.** an element that contains 14 electrons

$1s^2 2s^2 2p^6 3s^2 3p^2$

The element is silicon.

# Chapter 6

**For questions 1–5, do not use the periodic table.**

**1.** Write the electron configurations for the elements in periods 2–4 of group 2A.

period 2, group 2A: $1s^2 2s^2$

period 3, group 2A: $1s^2 2s^2 2p^6 3s^2$

period 4, group 2A: $1s^2 2s^2 2p^6 3s^2 3p^6 4s^2$

**2.** Determine the group, period, and block of the elements with the following electron configurations.

**a.** $[He]2s^2 2p^4$

group 6A, period 2, p-block

**b.** $[Xe]6s^1$

group 1A, period 6, s-block

**c.** $[Ar]4s^2 3d^{10} 4p^2$

group 4A, period 4, p-block

**3.** Categorize each of the elements in problem 2 as a representative element or a transition element.

All of the elements are representative elements.

**4.** Write the electron configuration of the element fitting each of the following descriptions. Use noble-gas notations.

**a.** Group 8A element in the third period

$[Ne]3s^2 3p^6$

**b.** Group 4A element in the fourth period

$[Ar]4s^2 3d^{10} 4p^2$

**c.** Halogen in the second period

$[He]2s^2 2p^5$

**d.** Group 1A element in the fourth period

$[Ar]4s^1$

**5.** What are the noble-gas notations of all the elements with the following valence electron configurations?

**a.** $s^2$

$1s^2$, $[He]2s^2$, $[Ne]3s^2$, $[Ar]4s^2$, $[Kr]5s^2$, $[Xe]6s^2$, $[Rn]7s^2$

**b.** $s^2 p^1$

$[He]2s^2 2p^1$, $[Ne]3s^2 3p^1$, $[Ar]4s^2 3d^{10} 4p^1$, $[Kr]5s^2 4d^{10} 5p^1$, $[Xe]6s^2 4f^{14} 5d^{10} 6p^1$

**For questions 6–9, do not use Figure 6-12, 6-15, or 6-20.**

**6.** Rank the following atoms in order of decreasing radii.

**a.** Al, Na, P, S

Na, Al, P, S

**b.** Al, Ga, In

In, Ga, Al

**c.** As, Ge, Ga

Ga, Ge, As

**d.** Br, Ca, Cl, K

K, Ca, Br, Cl

**7.** Rank the following ions in order of decreasing radii.

**a.** $Br^-$, $Cl^-$, $F^-$

$Br^-$, $Cl^-$, $F^-$

**b.** $Be^{2+}$, $Ca^{2+}$, $Mg^{2+}$

$Ca^{2+}$, $Mg^{2+}$, $Be^{2+}$

**c.** $Ca^{2+}$, $Ga^{3+}$, $K^+$

$K^+$, $Ca^{2+}$, $Ga^{3+}$

**8.** Rank the following particles in order of decreasing radii.

**a.** I, $I^-$

$I^-$, I

**b.** K, $K^+$

K, $K^+$

**c.** Al, $Al^{3+}$

Al, $Al^{3+}$

**9.** Rank the following atoms in order of decreasing electronegativity.

**a.** Na, Li, K

Li, Na, K

**b.** K, Sc, Ca

Sc, Ca, K

**c.** As, Sn, S

S, As, Sn

# Chapter 10

**Balance the following chemical equations.**

**1.** $SnS_2(s) + O_2(g) \rightarrow SnO_2(s) + SO_2(g)$

$SnS_2(s) + 3O_2(g) \rightarrow SnO_2(s) + 2SO_2(g)$

**2.** $C_2H_6(g) + O_2(g) \rightarrow CO_2(g) + H_2O(g)$

$2C_2H_6(g) + 7O_2(g) \rightarrow 4CO_2(g) + 6H_2O(g)$

**3.** $Al(s) + HCl(aq) \rightarrow AlCl_3(aq) + H_2(g)$

$2Al(s) + 6HCl(aq) \rightarrow 2AlCl_3(aq) + 3H_2(g)$

**4.** $CoCO_3(s) \rightarrow CoO(s) + CO_2(g)$

$CoCO_3(s) \rightarrow CoO(s) + CO_2(g)$

**Write a balanced equation for each of the following reactions, substituting symbols and formulas for names. Include the state of each reactant and product. Then identify the reaction type for each. If more than one reaction type applies, list all that apply.**

**5.** When aluminum nitrate and sodium hydroxide solutions are mixed, solid aluminum hydroxide forms. The other product is sodium nitrate.

$Al(NO_3)_3(aq) + 3NaOH(aq) \rightarrow Al(OH)_3(s) + 3NaNO_3(aq)$

double-replacement

**6.** When magnesium is heated in the presence of nitrogen gas, solid magnesium nitride forms.

$4Mg(s) + 3N_2(g) \rightarrow 2Mg_2N_3(s)$

synthesis

**7.** When solid copper(II) oxide and hydrogen react, metallic copper and water form.

$CuO(s) + H_2(g) \rightarrow Cu(s) + H_2O(l)$

single-replacement

**8.** Most industrial production of metallic sodium is accomplished by passing an electric current through molten sodium chloride. Chlorine gas also is produced.

$2NaCl(l) \rightarrow 2Na(s) + Cl_2(g)$

decomposition

**9.** Liquid pentane ($C_5H_{12}$) burns, producing water vapor and carbon dioxide.

$C_5H_{12}(l) + 8O_2(g) \rightarrow 6H_2O(g) + 5CO_2(g)$

combustion

**10.** When chlorine gas is passed through a potassium bromide solution, bromine forms in a potassium chloride solution.

$Cl_2(g) + 2KBr(aq) \rightarrow Br_2(l) + 2KCl(aq)$

single-replacement

**11.** Magnesium burns in air to form magnesium oxide.

$2Mg(s) + O_2(g) \rightarrow 2MgO(s)$

synthesis, combustion

**Predict the products in each of the following reactions. If no reaction occurs, write *NR*. You may use Figure 10-10 for the relative activities of common metals and halogens.**

**12.** Rb(s) + CaCl$_2$(aq)

RbCl(aq) + Ca(s)

**13.** Pt(s) + MnBr$_2$(aq)

NR

**14.** F$_2$(g) + NaI(aq)

NaF(aq) + I$_2$(s)

**15.** Zn(s) + AgNO$_3$(aq)

Ag(s) + Zn(NO$_3$)$_2$(aq)

**Write a complete ionic equation and a net ionic equation for each of the following double-displacement reactions.**

**16.** Ba(NO$_3$)$_2$(aq) + H$_2$SO$_4$(aq) →
        BaSO$_4$(s) + 2HNO$_3$(aq)

$Ba^{2+}(aq) + 2NO_3^{-}(aq) + 2H^{+}(aq) + SO_4^{2-}(aq) \rightarrow$
$BaSO_4(s) + 2H^{+}(aq) + 2NO_3^{-}(aq)$
$Ba^{2+}(aq) + SO_4^{2-}(aq) \rightarrow BaSO_4(s)$

**17.** FeCl$_3$(aq) + (NH$_4$)$_3$PO$_4$(aq) →
        FePO$_4$(s) + 3NH$_4$Cl(aq)

$Fe^{3+}(aq) + 3Cl^{-}(aq) + 3NH_4^{+}(aq) + PO_4^{3-}(aq) \rightarrow$
$FePO_4(s) + 3NH_4^{+}(aq) + 3Cl^{-}(aq)$
$Fe^{3+}(aq) + PO_4^{3-}(aq) \rightarrow FePO_4(s)$

**18.** KCl(aq) + AgC$_2$H$_3$O$_2$(aq) →
        AgCl(s) + KC$_2$H$_3$O$_2$(aq)

$K^{+}(aq) + Cl^{-}(aq) + Ag^{+}(aq) + C_2H_3O_2^{-}(aq) \rightarrow$
$AgCl(s) + K^{+}(aq) + C_2H_3O_2^{-}(aq)$
$Cl^{-}(aq) + Ag^{+}(aq) \rightarrow AgCl(s)$

# Chapter 11

**1.** Identify and calculate the number of representative particles in each of the following quantities.

   **a.** 2.15 moles of gold

$$2.15 \ \text{mol Au} \times \frac{6.02 \times 10^{23} \ \text{atoms Au}}{1 \ \text{mol Au}}$$

$$= 1.29 \times 10^{24} \ \text{atoms Au}$$

   **b.** 0.151 mole of nitrogen oxide

$$0.151 \ \text{mol NO} \times \frac{6.02 \times 10^{23} \ \text{molecules NO}}{1 \ \text{mol NO}}$$

$$= 9.09 \times 10^{22} \ \text{molecules NO}$$

   **c.** 11.5 moles of potassium bromide

$$11.5 \ \text{mol KBr} \times \frac{6.02 \times 10^{23} \ \text{formula units KBr}}{1 \ \text{mol KBr}}$$

$$= 6.92 \times 10^{24} \ \text{formula units KBr}$$

**2.** Calculate the number of moles of the substance that contains the following number of representative particles.

   **a.** $8.92 \times 10^{23}$ atoms of barium

$$8.92 \times 10^{23} \ \text{atoms Ba} \times \frac{1 \ \text{mol Ba}}{6.02 \times 10^{23} \ \text{atoms Ba}}$$

$$= 1.48 \ \text{mol Ba}$$

   **b.** $5.50 \times 10^{25}$ molecules of carbon monoxide

$$5.50 \times 10^{25} \ \text{molecules CO} \times$$

$$\frac{1 \ \text{mol CO}}{6.02 \times 10^{23} \ \text{molecules CO}}$$

$$= 91.4 \ \text{mol CO}$$

   **c.** $2.66 \times 10^{22}$ formula units of potassium iodide

$$2.66 \times 10^{22} \ \text{formula units KI} \times$$

$$\frac{1 \ \text{mol KI}}{6.02 \times 10^{23} \ \text{formula units KI}}$$

$$= 0.0442 \ \text{mol KI}$$

**3.** Determine the mass in grams of each of the following quantities.

   **a.** 1.24 moles of beryllium

$$1.24 \ \text{mol Be} \times \frac{9.01 \ \text{g Be}}{1 \ \text{mol Be}}$$

$$= 11.2 \ \text{g Be}$$

   **b.** 3.35 moles of calcium

$$3.35 \ \text{mol Ca} \times \frac{40.08 \ \text{g Ca}}{1 \ \text{mol Ca}}$$

$$= 134 \ \text{g Ca}$$

   **c.** 0.155 mole of sulfur

$$0.155 \ \text{mol S} \times \frac{32.07 \ \text{g S}}{1 \ \text{mol S}}$$

$$= 4.97 \ \text{g S}$$

**4.** Calculate the number of moles in each of the following quantities.

   **a.** 6.35 g lithium

$$6.35 \ \text{g Li} \times \frac{1 \ \text{mol Li}}{6.94 \ \text{g Li}}$$

$$= 0.915 \ \text{mol Li}$$

   **b.** 346 g zinc

$$346 \ \text{g Zn} \times \frac{1 \ \text{mol Zn}}{65.39 \ \text{g Zn}}$$

$$= 5.29 \ \text{mol Zn}$$

**c.** 115 g nickel

$$115 \text{ g Ni} \times \frac{1 \text{ mol Ni}}{58.69 \text{ g Ni}}$$

$$= 1.96 \text{ mol Ni}$$

**5.** How many atoms are in the following samples?

**a.** 1.24 g cobalt

$$1.24 \text{ g Co} \times \frac{1 \text{ mol Co}}{58.93 \text{ g Co}} \times$$

$$\frac{6.02 \times 10^{23} \text{ atoms Co}}{1 \text{ mol Co}}$$

$$= 1.27 \times 10^{22} \text{ atoms Co}$$

**b.** 0.575 g cesium

$$0.575 \text{ g Ce} \times \frac{1 \text{ mol Ce}}{132.91 \text{ g Ce}} \times$$

$$\frac{6.02 \times 10^{23} \text{ atoms Ce}}{1 \text{ mol Ce}}$$

$$= 2.60 \times 10^{21} \text{ atoms Ce}$$

**c.** 65.6 g silicon

$$65.6 \text{ g Si} \times \frac{1 \text{ mol Si}}{28.09 \text{ g Si}} \times$$

$$\frac{6.02 \times 10^{23} \text{ atoms Si}}{1 \text{ mol Si}}$$

$$= 1.41 \times 10^{24} \text{ atoms Si}$$

**6.** Which quantity has the greatest mass?

**a.** $4.16 \times 10^{23}$ atoms of radium

$$4.16 \times 10^{23} \text{ atoms Ra} \times \frac{1 \text{ mol Ra}}{6.02 \times 10^{23} \text{ atoms Ra}} \times$$

$$\frac{226 \text{ g Ra}}{1 \text{ mol Ra}}$$

$$= 156 \text{ g Ra}$$

**b.** $1.50 \times 10^{20}$ atoms of cadmium

$$1.50 \times 10^{20} \text{ atoms Cd} \times \frac{1 \text{ mol Cd}}{6.02 \times 10^{23} \text{ atoms Cd}} \times$$

$$\frac{112.41 \text{ g Cd}}{1 \text{ mol Cd}}$$

$$= 0.0280 \text{ g Cd}$$

**c.** $1.33 \times 10^{24}$ atoms of argon

$$1.33 \times 10^{24} \text{ atoms Ar} \times \frac{1 \text{ mol Ar}}{6.02 \times 10^{23} \text{ atoms Ar}} \times$$

$$\frac{39.95 \text{ g Ar}}{1 \text{ mol Ar}}$$

$$= 88.3 \text{ g Ar}$$

The quantity $4.16 \times 10^{23}$ atoms of radium has the greatest mass.

**7.** Calculate the number of moles in each of the following quantities.

**a.** atoms of each element in 3.35 moles of aspirin ($C_9H_8O_4$)

$$3.35 \text{ mol } C_9H_8O_4 \times \frac{9 \text{ mol C}}{1 \text{ mol } C_9H_8O_4} = 30.2 \text{ mol C}$$

$$3.35 \text{ mol } C_9H_8O_4 \times \frac{8 \text{ mol H}}{1 \text{ mol } C_9H_8O_4} = 26.8 \text{ mol H}$$

$$3.35 \text{ mol } C_9H_8O_4 \times \frac{4 \text{ mol O}}{1 \text{ mol } C_9H_8O_4} = 13.4 \text{ mol O}$$

**b.** positive and negative ions in 1.75 moles of calcium fluoride ($CaF_2$)

$$1.75 \text{ mol } CaF_2 \times \frac{1 \text{ mol } Ca^{2+}}{1 \text{ mol } CaF_2} = 1.75 \text{ mol } Ca^{2+}$$

$$1.75 \text{ mol } CaF_2 \times \frac{2 \text{ mol } F^-}{1 \text{ mol } CaF_2} = 3.50 \text{ mol } F^-$$

**8.** Determine the molar mass of each of the following compounds.

**a.** formic acid ($CH_2O_2$)

$$1 \text{ mol } CH_2O_2 \times \frac{1 \text{ mol } C}{1 \text{ mol } CH_2O_2} \times \frac{12.01 \text{ g } C}{1 \text{ mol } C}$$

$$= 12.01 \text{ g } C$$

$$1 \text{ mol } CH_2O_2 \times \frac{2 \text{ mol } H}{1 \text{ mol } CH_2O_2} \times \frac{1.01 \text{ g } H}{1 \text{ mol } H}$$

$$= 2.02 \text{ g } H$$

$$1 \text{ mol } CH_2O_2 \times \frac{2 \text{ mol } O}{1 \text{ mol } CH_2O_2} \times \frac{16.00 \text{ g } O}{1 \text{ mol } O}$$

$$= 32.00 \text{ g } O$$

$(12.01 \text{ g} + 2.02 \text{ g} + 32.00 \text{ g} ) = 46.03 \text{ g}$

The molar mass of formic acid is 46.03 g/mol.

**b.** ammonium dichromate (($NH_4)_2Cr_2O_7$)

$$1 \text{ mol } (NH_4)_2Cr_2O_7 \times \frac{2 \text{ mol } N}{1 \text{ mol } (NH_4)_2Cr_2O_7} \times$$

$$\frac{14.01 \text{ g } N}{1 \text{ mol } N} = 28.02 \text{ g } N$$

$$1 \text{ mol } (NH_4)_2Cr_2O_7 \times \frac{8 \text{ mol } H}{1 \text{ mol } (NH_4)_2Cr_2O_7} \times$$

$$\frac{1.01 \text{ g } H}{1 \text{ mol } H} = 8.08 \text{ g } H$$

$$1 \text{ mol } (NH_4)_2Cr_2O_7 \times \frac{2 \text{ mol } Cr}{1 \text{ mol } (NH_4)_2Cr_2O_7} \times$$

$$\frac{52.00 \text{ g } Cr}{1 \text{ mol } N} = 104.0 \text{ g } Cr$$

$$1 \text{ mol } (NH_4)_2Cr_2O_7 \times \frac{7 \text{ mol } O}{1 \text{ mol } (NH_4)_2Cr_2O_7} \times$$

$$\frac{16.00 \text{ g } O}{1 \text{ mol } O} = 112.0 \text{ g } O$$

$(28.02 \text{ g} + 8.08 \text{ g} + 104.00 \text{ g} + 112.0 \text{ g})$
$= 252.1 \text{ g}$

The molar mass of ammonium dichromate is 252.1 g/mol.

**9.** What is the mass in grams of each of the following quantities?

**a.** 2.53 moles of lead(II) nitrate ($Pb(NO_3)_2$)

$$1 \text{ mol } Pb(NO_3)_2 \times \frac{1 \text{ mol } Pb}{1 \text{ mol } Pb(NO_3)_2} \times$$

$$\frac{207.2 \text{ g } Pb}{1 \text{ mol } Pb} = 207.2 \text{ g } Pb$$

$$1 \text{ mol } Pb(NO_3)_2 \times \frac{2 \text{ mol } N}{1 \text{ mol } Pb(NO_3)_2} \times$$

$$\frac{14.01 \text{ g } N}{1 \text{ mol } N} = 28.02 \text{ g } N$$

$$1 \text{ mol } Pb(NO_3)_2 \times \frac{6 \text{ mol } O}{1 \text{ mol } Pb(NO_3)_2} \times$$

$$\frac{16.00 \text{ g } O}{1 \text{ mol } O} = 96.00 \text{ g } O$$

$(207.2 \text{ g} + 28.02 \text{ g} + 96.00 \text{ g}) = 331.2 \text{ g}$

The molar mass of lead(II) nitrate is 331.2 g/mol.

$$2.53 \text{ mol } Pb(NO_3)_2 \times \frac{331.2 \text{ g } Pb(NO_3)_2}{1 \text{ mol } Pb(NO_3)_2}$$

$$= 838 \text{ g}$$

The mass of 2.53 moles of lead(II) nitrate is 838 g.

**b.** 4.62 moles of magnesium bromide ($MgBr_2$)

$$1 \text{ mol } MgBr_2 \times \frac{1 \text{ mol } Mg}{1 \text{ mol } MgBr_2} \times$$

$$\frac{24.31 \text{ g } Mg}{1 \text{ mol } Mg} = 24.31 \text{ g } Mg$$

$$1 \text{ mol } MgBr_2 \times \frac{2 \text{ mol } Br}{1 \text{ mol } MgBr_2} \times$$

$$\frac{79.90 \text{ g } Br}{1 \text{ mol } Br} = 159.80 \text{ g } Br$$

$(24.31 \text{ g} + 159.80 \text{ g}) = 184.11 \text{ g}$

The molar mass of magnesium bromide is 184.11 g/mol.

$$4.62 \text{ mol } MgBr_2 \times \frac{184.11 \text{ g } MgBr_2}{1 \text{ mol } MgBr_2}$$

$$= 851 \text{ g}$$

The mass of 4.62 moles of magnesium bromide is 851 g.

**10.** Calculate the number of moles in each of the following samples.

**a.** 3.75 g calcium carbide ($CaC_2$)

$1 \text{ mol } CaC_2 \times \dfrac{2 \text{ mol } C}{1 \text{ mol } CaC_2} \times \dfrac{12.01 \text{ g C}}{1 \text{ mol } C}$

$= 24.02 \text{ g C}$

$1 \text{ mol } CaC_2 \times \dfrac{1 \text{ mol } Ca}{1 \text{ mol } CaC_2} \times \dfrac{40.08 \text{ g Ca}}{1 \text{ mol } Ca}$

$= 40.08 \text{ g Ca}$

$(24.02 \text{ g} + 40.08 \text{ g}) = 64.10 \text{ g}$

The molar mass of calcium carbide is 64.10 g/mol.

$3.75 \text{ g } CaC_2 \times \dfrac{1 \text{ mol } CaC_2}{64.10 \text{ g } CaC_2}$

$= 0.0585 \text{ mol } CaC_2$

**b.** 245 g aluminum nitrite ($Al(NO_2)_3$)

$1 \text{ mol } Al(NO_2)_3 \times \dfrac{1 \text{ mol } Al}{1 \text{ mol } Al(NO_2)_3} \times \dfrac{26.98 \text{ g Al}}{1 \text{ mol } Al}$

$= 26.98 \text{ g Al}$

$1 \text{ mol } Al(NO_2)_3 \times \dfrac{3 \text{ mol } N}{1 \text{ mol } Al(NO_2)_3} \times \dfrac{14.01 \text{ g N}}{1 \text{ mol } N}$

$= 42.03 \text{ g N}$

$1 \text{ mol } Al(NO_2)_3 \times \dfrac{6 \text{ mol } O}{1 \text{ mol } Al(NO_2)_3} \times \dfrac{16.00 \text{ g O}}{1 \text{ mol } O}$

$= 96.00 \text{ g O}$

$(26.98 \text{ g} + 42.03 \text{ g} + 96.00 \text{ g}) = 165.01 \text{ g}$

The molar mass of aluminum nitrite is 165.01 g/mol.

$245 \text{ g } Al(NO_2)_3 \times \dfrac{1 \text{ mol } Al(NO_2)_3}{165.01 \text{ g } Al(NO_2)_3}$

$= 1.48 \text{ mol } Al(NO_2)_3$

**11.** Determine the percent composition of each of the following compounds.

**a.** manganese oxide (MnO)

$1 \text{ mol } MnO \times \dfrac{1 \text{ mol } Mn}{1 \text{ mol } MnO} \times \dfrac{54.94 \text{ g Mn}}{1 \text{ mol } Mn}$

$= 54.94 \text{ g Mn}$

$1 \text{ mol } MnO \times \dfrac{1 \text{ mol } O}{1 \text{ mol } MnO} \times \dfrac{16.00 \text{ g O}}{1 \text{ mol } O}$

$= 16.00 \text{ g O}$

$(54.94 \text{ g} + 16.00 \text{ g}) = 70.94 \text{ g}$

The molar mass of manganese oxide is 70.94 g/mol.

$\textit{mass percent } Mn = \dfrac{54.94 \text{ g Mn}}{70.94 \text{ g MnO}} \times 100$

$= 77.45\% \text{ Mn}$

$\textit{mass percent } O = \dfrac{16.00 \text{ g O}}{70.94 \text{ g MnO}} \times 100$

$= 22.55\% \text{ O}$

**b.** propanol ($C_3H_8O$)

$1 \text{ mol } C_3H_8O \times \dfrac{3 \text{ mol } C}{1 \text{ mol } C_3H_8O} \times \dfrac{12.01 \text{ g C}}{1 \text{ mol } C}$

$= 36.03 \text{ g C}$

$1 \text{ mol } C_3H_8O \times \dfrac{8 \text{ mol } H}{1 \text{ mol } C_3H_8O} \times \dfrac{1.01 \text{ g H}}{1 \text{ mol } H}$

$= 8.08 \text{ g H}$

$1 \text{ mol } C_3H_8O \times \dfrac{1 \text{ mol } O}{1 \text{ mol } C_3H_8O} \times \dfrac{16.00 \text{ g O}}{1 \text{ mol } O}$

$= 16.00 \text{ g O}$

$(36.03 \text{ g} + 8.08 \text{ g} + 16.00 \text{ g}) = 60.11 \text{ g}$

The molar mass of propanol is 60.11 g/mol.

$\textit{mass percent } C = \dfrac{36.03 \text{ g C}}{60.11 \text{ g } C_3H_8O} \times 100$

$= 59.94\% \text{ C}$

$\textit{mass percent } H = \dfrac{8.08 \text{ g H}}{60.11 \text{ g } C_3H_8O} \times 100$

$= 13.44\% \text{ H}$

$\textit{mass percent } O = \dfrac{16.00 \text{ g O}}{60.11 \text{ g } C_3H_8O} \times 100$

$= 26.62\% \text{ O}$

**c.** calcium phosphate ($Ca_3(PO_4)_2$)

$$1 \text{ mol } Ca_3(PO_4)_2 \times \frac{3 \text{ mol } Ca}{1 \text{ mol } Ca_3(PO_4)_2} \times$$

$$\frac{40.08 \text{ g Ca}}{1 \text{ mol } Ca} = 120.24 \text{ g Ca}$$

$$1 \text{ mol } Ca_3(PO_4)_2 \times \frac{2 \text{ mol } P}{1 \text{ mol } Ca_3(PO_4)_2} \times$$

$$\frac{30.97 \text{ g P}}{1 \text{ mol } P} = 61.94 \text{ g P}$$

$$1 \text{ mol } Ca_3(PO_4)_2 \times \frac{8 \text{ mol } O}{1 \text{ mol } Ca_3(PO_4)_2} \times$$

$$\frac{16.00 \text{ g O}}{1 \text{ mol } O} = 128.00 \text{ g O}$$

(120.24 g + 61.94 g + 128.00 g) = 310.18 g

The molar mass of calcium phosphate is 310.18 g/mol.

*mass percent* Ca = $\frac{120.24 \text{ g Ca}}{310.18 \text{ g } Ca_3(PO_4)_2} \times 100$

= 38.76% Ca

*mass percent* P = $\frac{61.94 \text{ g P}}{310.18 \text{ g } Ca_3(PO_4)_2} \times 100$

= 19.97% P

*mass percent* O = $\frac{128.00 \text{ g O}}{310.18 \text{ g } Ca_3(PO_4)_2} \times 100$

= 41.27% O

**12.** Determine the empirical formula for a 100.00-g sample of a compound having the following percent composition.

**a.** 94.07% sulfur and 5.93% hydrogen

In a 100.00-g sample:
  mass of S = 94.07 g
  mass of H = 5.93 g

$$94.07 \text{ g S} \times \frac{1 \text{ mol S}}{32.07 \text{ g S}} = 2.93 \text{ mol S}$$

$$5.93 \text{ g H} \times \frac{1 \text{ mol H}}{1.01 \text{ g H}} = 5.87 \text{ mol H}$$

$$\frac{5.87 \text{ mol H}}{2.93 \text{ mol S}} = \frac{2.00 \text{ mol H}}{1.00 \text{ mol S}} = \frac{2 \text{ mol H}}{1 \text{ mol S}}$$

$$\frac{2.93 \text{ mol S}}{2.93 \text{ mol S}} = \frac{1.00 \text{ mol S}}{1.00 \text{ mol S}} = \frac{1 \text{ mol S}}{1 \text{ mol S}}$$

2 mol H : 1 mol S

The empirical formula is $H_2S$.

**b.** 80.68% mercury, 12.87% oxygen, and 6.45% sulfur

Mass of Hg = 80.68 g Hg
Mass of O = 12.87 g O
Mass of S = 6.45 g S

$$80.68 \text{ g Hg} \times \frac{1 \text{ mol Hg}}{200.59 \text{ g Hg}} = 0.4022 \text{ mol Hg}$$

$$12.87 \text{ g O} \times \frac{1 \text{ mol O}}{16.00 \text{ g O}} = 0.8044 \text{ mol O}$$

$$6.45 \text{ g S} \times \frac{1 \text{ mol S}}{32.07 \text{ g S}} = 0.2011 \text{ mol S}$$

$$\frac{0.4022 \text{ mol Hg}}{0.2011 \text{ mol S}} = \frac{2.000 \text{ mol Hg}}{1.000 \text{ mol S}} = \frac{2 \text{ mol Hg}}{1 \text{ mol S}}$$

$$\frac{0.8044 \text{ mol O}}{0.2011 \text{ mol S}} = \frac{4.000 \text{ mol O}}{1.000 \text{ mol S}} = \frac{4 \text{ mol O}}{1 \text{ mol S}}$$

$$\frac{0.2011 \text{ mol S}}{0.2011 \text{ mol S}} = \frac{1.000 \text{ mol S}}{1.000 \text{ mol S}} = \frac{1 \text{ mol S}}{1 \text{ mol S}}$$

2 mol Hg : 4 mol O : 1 mol S

The empirical formula is $Hg_2SO_4$.

**13.** A 48.30-g sample of an aluminum-iodine compound contains 3.20 g of aluminum. What is the empirical formula for the compound?

48.30 g compound − 3.20 g Al = 45.10 g I

$$3.20 \text{ g Al} \times \frac{1 \text{ mol Al}}{26.98 \text{ g Al}} = 0.1186 \text{ mol Al}$$

$$45.10 \text{ g I} \times \frac{1 \text{ mol I}}{126.90 \text{ g I}} = 0.3554 \text{ mol I}$$

$$\frac{0.3554 \text{ mol I}}{0.1186 \text{ mol Al}} = \frac{2.997 \text{ mol I}}{1.000 \text{ mol Al}} = \frac{3 \text{ mol I}}{1 \text{ mol Al}}$$

$$\frac{0.1186 \text{ mol Al}}{0.1186 \text{ mol Al}} = \frac{1.000 \text{ mol Al}}{1.000 \text{ mol Al}} = \frac{1 \text{ mol Al}}{1 \text{ mol Al}}$$

3 mol I : 1 mol Al

The empirical formula is $AlI_3$.

**14.** A 50.00-g sample of hydrated manganese(II) chloride yields 31.75 g of the anhydrous compound after heating. Determine the chemical formula and name the hydrate.

50.00 g hydrate − 31.75 g anhydrous compound = 18.25 g water

$$1 \text{ mol MnCl}_2 \times \frac{1 \text{ mol Mn}}{1 \text{ mol MnCl}_2} \times \frac{54.94 \text{ g Mn}}{1 \text{ mol Mn}}$$
$$= 54.94 \text{ g Mn}$$

$$1 \text{ mol MnCl}_2 \times \frac{2 \text{ mol Cl}}{1 \text{ mol MnCl}_2} \times \frac{35.45 \text{ g Cl}}{1 \text{ mol Cl}}$$
$$= 70.90 \text{ g Cl}$$

(54.94 g + 70.90 g) = 125.84 g

The molar mass of manganese(II) chloride is 125.84 g/mol.

$$31.75 \text{ g MnCl}_2 \times \frac{1 \text{ mol MnCl}_2}{125.84 \text{ g MnCl}_2}$$
$$= 0.2523 \text{ mol MnCl}_2$$

$$18.25 \text{ g H}_2\text{O} \times \frac{1 \text{ mol H}_2\text{O}}{18.02 \text{ g H}_2\text{O}}$$
$$= 1.013 \text{ mol H}_2\text{O}$$

$$\frac{1.013 \text{ mol H}_2\text{O}}{0.2523 \text{ mol MnCl}_2} = \frac{4.015 \text{ mol H}_2\text{O}}{1.000 \text{ mol MnCl}_2}$$

$$= \frac{4 \text{ mol H}_2\text{O}}{1 \text{ mol Mn Cl}_2}$$

The ratio of water to manganese dichloride is 4 : 1. The chemical formula of the hydrate is $MnCl_2 \cdot 4H_2O$ and its name is manganese(II) chloride tetrahydrate.

**15.** Caffeine is a compound found in some natural coffees and teas and in some colas.

**a.** Determine the empirical formula for caffeine, using the following composition of a 100.00-g sample.
49.47 grams of carbon, 28.85 grams of nitrogen, 16.48 grams of oxygen, and 5.20 grams of hydrogen

$$49.47 \text{ g C} \times \frac{1 \text{ mol C}}{12.01 \text{ g C}} = 4.119 \text{ mol C}$$

$$28.85 \text{ g N} \times \frac{1 \text{ mol N}}{14.01 \text{ g N}} = 2.059 \text{ mol N}$$

$$16.48 \text{ g O} \times \frac{1 \text{ mol O}}{16.00 \text{ g O}} = 1.030 \text{ mol O}$$

$$5.20 \text{ g H} \times \frac{1 \text{ mol H}}{1.01 \text{ g H}} = 5.15 \text{ mol H}$$

$$\frac{4.119 \text{ mol C}}{1.030 \text{ mol O}} = \frac{3.999 \text{ mol C}}{1.000 \text{ mol O}} = \frac{4 \text{ mol C}}{1 \text{ mol O}}$$

$$\frac{2.059 \text{ mol N}}{1.030 \text{ mol O}} = \frac{1.999 \text{ mol N}}{1.000 \text{ mol O}} = \frac{2 \text{ mol N}}{1 \text{ mol O}}$$

$$\frac{5.15 \text{ mol H}}{1.030 \text{ mol O}} = \frac{5.00 \text{ mol H}}{1.00 \text{ mol O}} = \frac{5 \text{ mol H}}{1 \text{ mol O}}$$

$$\frac{1.030 \text{ mol O}}{1.030 \text{ mol O}} = \frac{1.000 \text{ mol O}}{1.000 \text{ mol O}} = \frac{1 \text{ mol O}}{1 \text{ mol O}}$$

4 mol C : 2 mol N : 5 mol H : 1 mol O

The empirical formula of caffeine is $C_4H_5N_2O$.

**b.** If the molar mass of caffeine is 194.19 g/mol, calculate its molecular formula.

$$4 \text{ mol C} \times \frac{12.01 \text{ g C}}{1 \text{ mol C}} = 48.04 \text{ g C}$$

$$2 \text{ mol N} \times \frac{14.01 \text{ g N}}{1 \text{ mol N}} = 28.02 \text{ g N}$$

$$5 \text{ mol H} \times \frac{1.01 \text{ g H}}{1 \text{ mol H}} = 5.05 \text{ g H}$$

$$1 \text{ mol O} \times \frac{16.00 \text{ g O}}{1 \text{ mol O}} = 16.00 \text{ g O}$$

(48.04 g + 28.02 g + 5.05 g + 16.00 g) = 97.11 g

The molar mass of the empirical formula is 97.11 g/mol.

$$n = \frac{\text{molar mass of compound}}{\text{molar mass of empirical formula}}$$

$$= \frac{194.19 \text{ g/mol}}{97.11 \text{ g/mol}} = 2.00$$

The molecular formula for caffeine is $(C_4H_5N_2O)2$, which is $C_8H_{10}N_4O_2$

# Chapter 12

1. Silicon nitride is used in the manufacturing of high-temperature thermal insulation for heat engines and turbines. It is produced by the following reaction.

$$3Si(s) + 2N_2(g) \rightarrow Si_3N_4(s)$$

a. Interpret the equation in terms of particles, moles, and masses.

Particles:

3 silicon atoms + 2 nitrogen molecules → 1 formula unit silicon nitride

Moles:

$3 \text{ mol Si} + 2 \text{ mol N}_2 \rightarrow 1 \text{ mol Si}_3N_4$

Masses:

$3 \text{ mol Si} \times \dfrac{28.09 \text{ g Si}}{1 \text{ mol Si}} = 84.27 \text{ g Si}$

$2 \text{ mol N}_2 \times \dfrac{28.02 \text{ g N}_2}{1 \text{ mol N}_2} = 56.04 \text{ g N}_2$

$1 \text{ mol Si}_3N_4 \times \dfrac{140.11 \text{ g Si}_3N_4}{1 \text{ mol Si}_3N_4} = 140.31 \text{ g Si}_3N_4$

$84.27 \text{ g Si} + 56.04 \text{ g N}_2 \rightarrow 140.31 \text{ g Si}_3N_4$

b. Show that mass is conserved in the reaction.

Mass of reactants: 84.27 g + 56.04 g = 140.31 g

Mass of product: 140.31 g

Because the mass of the product is equal to the total mass of the reactants, mass is conserved in the reaction.

2. The heat from a welder's torch is produced by the burning of acetylene gas. The reaction is represented by the following balanced chemical equation.

$$2C_2H_2(g) + 5O_2(g) \rightarrow 4CO_2(g) + 2H_2O(g)$$

Calculate the mole ratios from the balanced equation.

$\dfrac{5 \text{ mol O}_2}{2 \text{ mol C}_2H_2}$  $\dfrac{4 \text{ mol CO}_2}{2 \text{ mol C}_2H_2}$  $\dfrac{2 \text{ mol H}_2O}{2 \text{ mol C}_2H_2}$

$\dfrac{2 \text{ mol C}_2H_2}{5 \text{ mol O}_2}$  $\dfrac{4 \text{ mol CO}_2}{5 \text{ mol O}_2}$  $\dfrac{2 \text{ mol H}_2O}{5 \text{ mol O}_2}$

$\dfrac{2 \text{ mol C}_2H_2}{4 \text{ mol CO}_2}$  $\dfrac{5 \text{ mol O}_2}{4 \text{ mol CO}_2}$  $\dfrac{2 \text{ mol H}_2O}{4 \text{ mol CO}_2}$

$\dfrac{2 \text{ mol C}_2H_2}{2 \text{ mol H}_2O}$  $\dfrac{5 \text{ mol O}_2}{2 \text{ mol H}_2O}$  $\dfrac{4 \text{ mol CO}_2}{2 \text{ mol H}_2O}$

3. Limestone ($CaCO_3$) is treated with hydrochloric acid and water to manufacture calcium chloride hexahydrate. This compound is used to melt ice and snow on pavements and roads. The following balanced chemical equation represents the reaction.

$$CaCO_3(s) + 2HCl(aq) + 5H_2O(l) \rightarrow$$
$$CaCl_2 \cdot 6H_2O(s) + CO_2(g)$$

a. How many moles of calcium chloride hexahydrate will be produced from 4.00 mol calcium carbonate?

$4.00 \text{ mol CaCO}_3 \times \dfrac{1 \text{ mol CaCl}_2 \cdot 6H_2O}{1 \text{ mol CaCO}_3}$

$= 4.00 \text{ mol CaCl}_2 \cdot 6H_2O$

b. How many moles of hydrogen chloride will be needed to produce 1.25 mol of the hydrate?

$1.25 \text{ mol CaCl}_2 \cdot 6H_2O \times \dfrac{2 \text{ mol HCl}}{1 \text{ mol CaCl}_2 \cdot 6H_2O}$

$= 2.50 \text{ mol HCl}$

c. If 8.33 mol water is available for the reaction, how many moles of carbon dioxide will be released?

$8.33 \text{ mol H}_2O \times \dfrac{1 \text{ mol CO}_2}{5 \text{ mol H}_2O}$

$= 1.67 \text{ mol CO}_2$

**4.** To prevent corrosion and make paints adhere better, some aluminum products are treated with chromium(III) phosphate before finishing. Chromium(III) phosphate ($CrPO_4$) is commercially produced by treating chromium metal with orthophosphoric acid ($H_3PO_4$).

**a.** Balance the following equation for the reaction.

_____2_____$Cr(s)$ + _____2_____$H_3PO_4(aq) \rightarrow$

_____3_____$H_2(g)$ + _____2_____$CrPO_4(s)$

**b.** How many moles of chromium metal are needed to produce 855 g of chromium(III) phosphate?

$$855 \text{ g } CrPO_4 \times \frac{1 \text{ mol } CrPO_4}{146.97 \text{ g } CrPO_4}$$

$$= 5.82 \text{ mol } CrPO_4$$

$$5.82 \text{ mol } CrPO_4 \times \frac{2 \text{ mol } Cr}{2 \text{ mol } CrPO_4}$$

$$= 5.82 \text{ mol } Cr$$

**c.** The reaction of 206 g chromium will release how many moles of hydrogen gas?

$$206 \text{ g } Cr \times \frac{1 \text{ mol } Cr}{52.00 \text{ g } Cr} = 3.96 \text{ mol } Cr$$

$$3.96 \text{ mol } Cr \times \frac{3 \text{ mol } H_2}{2 \text{ mol } Cr} = 5.94 \text{ mol } H_2$$

**5.** Sand (silicon dioxide) and coke (carbon) are combined to form silicon carbide (SiC), a compound used in high-strength ceramic materials.

**a.** Balance the following equation for the reaction.

_____1_____$SiO_2(s)$ + _____3_____$C(s) \rightarrow$

_____1_____$SiC(s)$ + _____2_____$CO(g)$

**b.** What mass of silicon carbide will be produced from the reaction of 352 g silicon dioxide?

$$352 \text{ g } SiO_2 \times \frac{1 \text{ mol } SiO_2}{60.09 \text{ g } SiO_2} = 5.86 \text{ mol } SiO_2$$

$$5.86 \text{ mol } SiO_2 \times \frac{1 \text{ mol } SiC}{1 \text{ mol } SiO_2} = 5.86 \text{ mol } SiC$$

$$5.86 \text{ mol } SiC \times \frac{40.10 \text{ g } SiC}{1 \text{ mol } SiC} = 235 \text{ g } SiC$$

**c.** If 1.00 g of carbon is reacted, what mass of carbon monoxide is released?

$$1.00 \text{ g } C \times \frac{1 \text{ mol } C}{12.01 \text{ g } C} = 0.0833 \text{ mol } C$$

$$0.0833 \text{ mol } C \times \frac{2 \text{ mol } CO}{3 \text{ mol } C} = 0.0555 \text{ mol } CO$$

$$0.0555 \text{ mol } CO \times \frac{28.01 \text{ g } CO}{1 \text{ mol } CO} = 1.55 \text{ g } CO$$

**6.** Two compounds of nitrogen, nitrogen tetroxide ($N_2O_4$) and hydrazine ($N_2H_4$), are used as rocket fuels. When the two compounds are mixed, they ignite spontaneously and produce nitrogen gas and water.

**a.** Balance the following equation for the reaction.

_____1_____$N_2O_4(l)$ + _____2_____$N_2H_4(l) \rightarrow$

_____3_____$N_2(g)$ + _____4_____$H_2O(g)$

**b.** If 8.00 g nitrogen tetroxide and 4.00 g hydrazine are mixed, determine the following quantities.

1. limiting reactant

*balanced equation mole ratio*

$$= \frac{2 \text{ mol } N_2H_4}{1 \text{ mol } N_2O_4} = 2$$

$$8.00 \text{ g N}_2\text{O}_4 \times \frac{1 \text{ mol N}_2\text{O}_4}{92.02 \text{ g N}_2\text{O}_4}$$

$$= 0.0869 \text{ mol N}_2\text{O}_4$$

$$4.00 \text{ g N}_2\text{H}_4 \times \frac{1 \text{ mol N}_2\text{H}_4}{32.06 \text{ g N}_2\text{H}_4}$$

$$= 0.125 \text{ mol N}_2\text{H}_4$$

$$actual\ mole\ ratio = \frac{0.125 \text{ mol N}_2\text{H}_4}{0.0869 \text{ mol N}_2\text{O}_4} = 1.44$$

Because the actual mole ratio is less than the balanced equation mole ratio, the limiting reactant is hydrazine.

2. mass of product ($N_2$)

$$0.125 \text{ mol N}_2\text{H}_4 \times \frac{3 \text{ mol N}_2}{2 \text{ mol N}_2\text{H}_4} = 0.188 \text{ mol N}_2$$

$$0.188 \text{ mol N}_2 \times \frac{28.02 \text{ g N}_2}{1 \text{ mol N}_2} = 5.27 \text{ g N}_2$$

3. mass of excess reactant

$$0.125 \text{ mol N}_2\text{H}_4 \times \frac{1 \text{ mol N}_2\text{O}_4}{2 \text{ mol N}_2\text{H}_4}$$

$$= 0.0625 \text{ mol N}_2\text{O}_4$$

$$0.0625 \text{ mol N}_2\text{O}_4 \times \frac{92.02 \text{ g N}_2\text{O}_4}{1 \text{ mol N}_2\text{O}_4}$$

$$= 5.75 \text{ g N}_2\text{O}_4$$

$$8.00 \text{ g N}_2\text{O}_4 - 5.75 \text{ g N}_2\text{O}_4 = 2.25 \text{ g N}_2\text{O}_4$$

7. One step in the industrial refining of nickel is the decomposition of nickel carbonyl ($Ni(CO)_4$) into nickel and carbon monoxide. In a laboratory reaction, 25.0 g nickel carbonyl yielded 5.34 g nickel.

a. Balance the following equation for the reaction.

_____1_____ $Ni(CO)_4(g) \rightarrow$

_____1_____ $Ni(s) +$ _____4_____ $CO(g)$

b. Determine the theoretical yield of nickel.

$$25.0 \text{ g Ni(CO)}_4 \times \frac{1 \text{ mol Ni(CO)}_4}{170.73 \text{ g Ni(CO)}_4}$$

$$= 0.146 \text{ mol Ni(CO)}_4$$

$$0.146 \text{ mol Ni(CO)}_4 \times \frac{1 \text{ mol Ni}}{1 \text{ mol Ni(CO)}_4}$$

$$= 0.146 \text{ mol Ni}$$

$$0.146 \text{ mol Ni} \times \frac{58.69 \text{ g Ni}}{1 \text{ mol Ni}} = 8.57 \text{ g Ni}$$

c. Determine the percent yield.

$$percent\ yield = \frac{actual\ yield}{theoretical\ yield} \times 100$$

$$= \frac{5.34 \text{ g Ni}}{8.57 \text{ g Ni}} \times 100 = 62.3\%$$

# Chapter 13

1. Calculate the ratio of effusion rates of oxygen ($O_2$) to hydrogen ($H_2$).

$$\frac{\text{Rate}_{O_2}}{\text{Rate}_{H_2}} = \frac{\sqrt{\text{molar mass}_{H_2}}}{\sqrt{\text{molar mass}_{O_2}}} = \frac{\sqrt{2.02 \text{ g/mol}}}{\sqrt{32.00 \text{ g/mol}}}$$

$$= \frac{1.42}{5.657} = 0.251$$

2. Methane ($CH_4$) effuses at a rate of 2.45 mol/s. What will be the effusion rate of argon (Ar) under the same conditions?

$$\frac{\text{Rate}_{Ar}}{\text{Rate}_{CH_4}} = \frac{\sqrt{\text{molar mass}_{CH_4}}}{\sqrt{\text{molar mass}_{Ar}}}$$

$$\text{Rate}_{Ar} = \text{Rate}_{CH_4} \times \frac{\sqrt{\text{molar mass}_{CH_4}}}{\sqrt{\text{molar mass}_{Ar}}}$$

$$= 2.45 \text{ mol/s} \times \frac{\sqrt{16.05 \text{ g/mol}}}{\sqrt{39.95 \text{ g/mol}}}$$

$$= 2.45 \text{ mol/s} \times \frac{4.006}{6.321}$$

$$= 1.55 \text{ mol/s}$$

**3.** The effusion rate of hydrogen sulfide ($H_2S$) is 1.50 mol/s. Another gas under similar conditions effuses at a rate of 1.25 mol/s. What is the molar mass of the second gas?

$$\frac{\text{Rate}_{H_2S}}{\text{Rate}_{unknown}} = \frac{\sqrt{\text{molar mass}_{unknown}}}{\sqrt{\text{molar mass}_{H_2S}}}$$

$$\frac{(\text{Rate}_{H_2S})^2}{(\text{Rate}_{unknown})^2} = \frac{\text{molar mass}_{unknown}}{\text{molar mass}_{H_2S}}$$

$$\text{molar mass}_{unknown} = \text{molar mass}_{H_2S} \times \frac{(\text{Rate}_{H_2S})^2}{(\text{Rate}_{unknown})^2}$$

$$= 34.09 \text{ g/mol} \times \frac{(1.50 \text{ mol/s})^2}{(1.25 \text{ mol/s})^2}$$

$$= 34.09 \text{ g/mol} \times \frac{2.25}{1.56}$$

$$= 49.2 \text{ g/mol}$$

**4.** The pressure of a gas in a manometer is 12.9 mm Hg. Express this value in each of the following units.

**a.** torr

$$12.9 \text{ mm Hg} \times \frac{1 \text{ torr}}{1 \text{ mm Hg}} = 12.9 \text{ torr}$$

**b.** atmosphere

$$12.9 \text{ mm Hg} \times \frac{1 \text{ atm}}{760 \text{ mm Hg}} = 1.70 \times 10^{-2} \text{ atm}$$

**c.** kilopascal

$$12.9 \text{ mm Hg} \times \frac{1 \text{ kPa}}{7.501 \text{ mm Hg}} = 1.72 \text{ kPa}$$

**5.** The vapor pressure of water is 2.3 kPa at 23°C. What is the vapor pressure of water at this temperature expressed in atmospheres?

$$2.3 \text{ kPa} \times \frac{1 \text{ atm}}{101.3 \text{ kPa}} = 2.3 \times 10^{-2} \text{ atm}$$

**6.** What is the pressure of a mixture of nitrogen ($N_2$) and oxygen ($O_2$) if the partial pressure of $N_2$ is 594 mm Hg and the partial pressure of $O_2$ is 165 mm Hg?

$$P_{total} = P_{N_2} + P_{O_2}$$
$$= 594 \text{ mm Hg} + 165 \text{ mm Hg}$$
$$= 759 \text{ mm Hg}$$

**7.** A sample of air is collected at 101.1 kPa. If the partial pressure of water vapor in the sample is 2.8 kPa, what is the partial pressure of the dry air?

$$P_{total} = P_{dry \ air} + P_{water \ vapor}$$
$$P_{dry \ air} = P_{total} - P_{water \ vapor}$$
$$= 101.1 \text{ kPa} - 2.8 \text{ kPa}$$
$$= 98.3 \text{ kPa}$$

**8.** Suppose that 5-mL containers of helium (He), neon (Ne), and argon (Ar) are at pressures of 1 atm, 2 atm, and 3 atm, respectively. The He and Ne are then added to the container of Ar.

**a.** What is the partial pressure of He in the container after the three gases are mixed?

1 atm

**b.** What is the total pressure in the container after the three gases are mixed?

$$P_{total} = P_{He} + P_{Ne} + P_{Ar}$$
$$= 1 \text{ atm} + 2 \text{ atm} + 3 \text{ atm}$$
$$= 6 \text{ atm}$$

# Chapter 14

**1.** In one city, a balloon with a volume of 6.0 L is filled with air at 101 kPa pressure. The balloon in then taken to a second city at a much higher altitude. At this second city, atmospheric pressure is only 91 kPa. If the temperature is the same in both places, what will be the new volume of the balloon?

$$P_1V_1 = P_2V_2; \ V_2 = \frac{P_1V_1}{P_2}; \ V_2 = \frac{(101 \text{ kPa})(6.0 \text{ L})}{91 \text{ kPa}}$$

$$= 6.7 \text{ L}$$

**2.** A certain mass of gas in a 2.25-L container has a pressure of 164 kPa. What will the new pressure be if the volume of the container is reduced to 1.50 L and the temperature stays constant?

$$P_1V_1 = P_2V_2; \ P_2 = \frac{P_1V_1}{V_2}; \ P_2 = \frac{(164 \text{ kPa})(2.25 \text{ L})}{1.50 \text{ L}}$$

$$= 246 \text{ kPa}$$

**3.** If 5.80 dm$^3$ of gas is collected at a pressure of 92.0 kPa, what volume will the same gas occupy at 101.3 kPa if the temperature stays constant?

$$P_1V_1 = P_2V_2; \ V_2 = \frac{P_1V_1}{P_2}; \ V_2$$

$$= \frac{(92.0 \text{ kPa})(5.80 \text{ dm}^3)}{101.3 \text{ kPa}} = 5.27 \text{ dm}^3$$

**4.** If the volume of an air pump used to inflate a football decreases from 480 mL to 375 mL, and the original pressure was 93.5 kPa, what is the new air pressure in the pump if the temperature stays constant?

$$P_1V_1 = P_2V_2; \ P_2 = \frac{P_1V_1}{V_2}; \ P_2 = \frac{(93.5 \text{ kPa})(480 \text{ mL})}{375 \text{ mL}}$$

$$= 120 \text{ kPa}$$

**5.** Maintaining constant pressure, the volume of a gas is increased from 18.0 dm$^3$ to 32.0 dm$^3$ by heating it. If the original temperature was 18.0°C, what is the new temperature in degrees Celsius?

$$\frac{V_1}{T_1} = \frac{V_2}{T_2}; \ T_2 = \frac{V_2T_1}{V_1}; \ T_2 = \frac{(32.0 \text{ dm}^3)(291 \text{ K})}{18.0 \text{ dm}^3}$$

$$= 517 \text{ K} = 244°C$$

**6.** A natural gas tank is constructed so that the pressure remains constant. On a hot day when the temperature was 33°C, the volume of gas in the tank was determined to be 3000.0 L. What would the volume be on a warm day when the temperature is 11°C?

$$\frac{V_1}{T_1} = \frac{V_2}{T_2}; \ V_2 = \frac{V_1T_2}{T_1}; \ V_2 = \frac{(3000.0 \text{ L})(284 \text{ K})}{306 \text{ K}}$$

$$= 2780 \text{ L}$$

**7.** A 50.0-mL sample of gas is cooled from 119°C to 80.0°C. If the pressure remains constant, what is the final volume of the gas?

$$\frac{V_1}{T_1} = \frac{V_2}{T_2}; \ V_2 = \frac{V_1T_2}{T_1}; \ V_2 = \frac{(50.0 \text{ mL})(353 \text{ K})}{392 \text{ K}}$$

$$= 45.0 \text{ mL}$$

**8.** A 10.0-L cylinder of gas is stored at room temperature (20.0°C) and a pressure of 1800 psi. If the gas is transferred to a 6.0-L cylinder, at what Celsius temperature would it have to be stored in order for the pressure to remain at 1800 psi?

$$\frac{V_1}{T_1} = \frac{V_2}{T_2}; \ T_2 = \frac{V_2T_1}{V_1}; \ T_2 = \frac{(6.0 \text{ L})(293 \text{ K})}{10.0 \text{ L}}$$

$$= 176 \text{ K} = -97°C$$

**9.** If the gas pressure in an aerosol can is 148.5 kPa at 23°C, what is the pressure inside the can if it is heated to 298°C?

$$\frac{P_1}{T_1} = \frac{P_2}{T_2}; P_2 = \frac{P_1 T_2}{T_1}; P_2 = \frac{(148.5 \text{ kPa})(571 \text{ K})}{296 \text{ K}}$$

$$= 286 \text{ kPa}$$

**10.** A tank for compressed gas has a maximum safe pressure limit of 850 kPa. The pressure gauge reads 425 kPa when the temperature is 28°C. What is the highest temperature in degrees Celsius the tank can withstand safely?

$$\frac{P_1}{T_1} = \frac{P_2}{T_2}; T_2 = \frac{T_1 P_2}{P_1}; T_2 = \frac{(301 \text{ K})(850 \text{ kPa})}{425 \text{ kPa}}$$

$$= 602 \text{ K} = 330°C$$

**11.** In a steel container, it was found that the pressure of the gas inside was 160 kPa when the container had been heated to 98°C. What had been the pressure of the gas when the temperature had been 50°C the previous day?

$$\frac{P_1}{T_1} = \frac{P_2}{T_2}; P_1 = \frac{P_2 T_1}{T_2}; P_1 = \frac{(160 \text{ kPa})(323 \text{ K})}{371 \text{ K}}$$

$$= 140 \text{ kPa}$$

**12.** A steel cylinder is filled with a gas at a temperature of 25.0°C and a pressure of 225.0 kPa. What will the pressure be if the temperature is raised to 47°C?

$$\frac{P_1}{T_1} = \frac{P_2}{T_2}; P_2 = \frac{P_1 T_2}{T_1}; P_2 = \frac{(225.0 \text{ kPa})(320.0 \text{ K})}{298 \text{ K}}$$

$$= 242 \text{ kPa}$$

**13.** A balloon is filled with gas at a pressure of 102.3 kPa and a temperature of 45.5°C. Its volume under these conditions is 12.5 L. The balloon is then taken into a decompression chamber where the volume is measured as 2.50 L. If the temperature is 36.0°C, what is the pressure in the chamber?

$$\frac{P_1 V_1}{T_1} = \frac{P_2 V_2}{T_2}; P_2 = \frac{P_1 V_1 T_2}{T_1 V_2}; P_2 =$$

$$\frac{(102.3 \text{ kPa})(12.5 \text{ L})(309 \text{ K})}{(318.5 \text{ K})(2.50 \text{ L})} = 496 \text{ kPa}$$

**14.** A weather balloon contains 14.0 L of helium at a pressure of 95.5 kPa and a temperature of 12.0°C. If this had been stored in a 1.50-L cylinder at 21.0°C, what must the pressure in the cylinder have been?

$$\frac{P_1 V_1}{T_1} = \frac{P_2 V_2}{T_2}; P_1 = \frac{P_2 V_2 T_1}{V_1 T_2}; P_1 =$$

$$\frac{(95.5 \text{ kPa})(14.0 \text{ L})(294 \text{ K})}{(1.50 \text{ L})(285 \text{ K})} = 919 \text{ kPa}$$

**15.** How many moles of a gas will occupy 2.50 L at STP?

$$n = \frac{V(1 \text{ mol})}{22.4 \text{ L}}; n = \frac{(2.50 \text{ L})(1 \text{ mol})}{22.4 \text{ L}} = 0.112 \text{ mol}$$

**16.** Calculate the volume that 3.60 g $H_2$ gas will occupy at STP.

$$n = \frac{m}{M} = \frac{3.60 \text{ g}}{2.02 \text{ g/mol}} = 1.78 \text{ mol};$$

$$V = 1.78 \text{ mol}\left(\frac{22.4 \text{ L}}{1 \text{ mol}}\right) = 39.9 \text{ L}$$

**17.** What volume is occupied by 0.580 mol of gas at 98.4 kPa and 11°C?

$$PV = nRT; V = \frac{nRT}{P};$$

$$V = \frac{(0.580 \text{ mol})(8.31 \text{ L·kPa/mol·K})(284 \text{ K})}{98.4 \text{ kPa}}$$

$$= 13.9 \text{ L}$$

**18.** When a sample of a gas was placed in a sealed container with a volume of 3.35 L and heated to 105°C, the gas vaporized and the resulting pressure inside the container was 170.0 kPa. How many moles of the gas was present?

$$PV = nRT; \; n = \frac{PV}{RT};$$

$$n = \frac{(170.0 \text{ kPa})(3.35 \text{ L})}{(8.31 \text{ L·kPa/mol·K})(378 \text{ K})}$$

$$= 0.181 \text{ mol}$$

**19.** An engineer wishes to design a container that will hold 14.0 mol of gas at a pressure no greater than 550 kPa and a temperature of 48°C. What is the minimum volume the container can have?

$$PV = nRT; \; V = \frac{nRT}{P};$$

$$V = \frac{(14.0 \text{ mol})(8.31 \text{ L·kPa/mol·K})(321 \text{ K})}{550 \text{ kPa}}$$

$$= 67.9 \text{ L}$$

**20.** What is the molar mass of a sample of gas that has a density of 2.85 g/L at 101 kPa pressure and 29°C?

$$M = \frac{DRT}{P};$$

$$M = \frac{(2.85 \text{ g/L})(8.31 \text{ L·kPa/mol·K})(302 \text{ K})}{101 \text{ kPa}}$$

$$= 70.8 \text{ g/mol}$$

**21.** How many grams of gas are present in a sample that has a molar mass of 44 g/mol and occupies a 1.8-L container at 108 kPa and 26.7°C?

$$m = \frac{MPV}{RT}; \; m = \frac{(44 \text{ g/mol})(108 \text{ kPa})(1.8 \text{ L})}{(8.31 \text{ L·kPa/mol·K})(299.7 \text{ K})}$$

$$= 3.4 \text{ g}$$

**22.** What is the molar mass of a gas if 142 g of the gas occupies a volume of 45.1 L at 28.4°C and 94.6 kPa?

$$PV = \frac{mRT}{M}; \; M = \frac{mRT}{PV};$$

$$M = \frac{(142 \text{ g})(8.31 \text{ L·kPa/mol·K})(301.4 \text{ K})}{(94.6 \text{ kPa·}45.1 \text{ L})}$$

$$= 83.4 \text{ g/mol}$$

**23.** Determine the volume of hydrogen gas needed to make 8 L of water vapor.

$$2H_2(g) + O_2(g) \rightarrow 2H_2O(g);$$

$$(8 \text{ L H}_2\text{O})\left(\frac{2 \text{ volumes H}_2}{2 \text{ volumes H}_2\text{O}}\right) = 8 \text{ L H}_2$$

**24.** Calculate the volume of chlorine gas at STP that is required to completely react with 3.50 g of silver, using the following equation: $2Ag(s) + Cl_2(g) \rightarrow 2AgCl(s)$.

$$3.50 \text{ g Ag}\left(\frac{1 \text{ mol Ag}}{107 \text{ g Ag}}\right)\left(\frac{1 \text{ mol Cl}_2}{2 \text{ mol Ag}}\right)\left(\frac{22.4 \text{ L Cl}_2}{1 \text{ mol Cl}_2}\right)$$

$$= 0.366 \text{ L Cl}_2$$

**25.** Use the reaction shown to calculate the mass of iron that must be used to obtain 0.500 L of hydrogen at STP.

$$3Fe(s) + 4H_2O(l) \rightarrow Fe_3O_4(s) + 4H_2(g)$$

$$(0.500 \text{ L H}_2)\left(\frac{1 \text{ mol H}_2}{22.4 \text{ L H}_2}\right)\left(\frac{3 \text{ mol Fe}}{4 \text{ mol H}_2}\right)\left(\frac{55.8 \text{ g Fe}}{1 \text{ mol Fe}}\right)$$

$$= 0.934 \text{ g Fe}$$

# Chapter 15

**1.** The solubility of a gas is 0.34 g/L at STP. What is its solubility at a pressure of 0.80 atm and the same temperature?

$$\frac{S_1}{P_1} = \frac{S_2}{P_2}$$

$$S_2 = S_1\frac{P_2}{P_1} = 0.34 \text{ g/L}\left(\frac{0.80 \text{ atm}}{1.0 \text{ atm}}\right) = 0.27 \text{ g/L}$$

$$S_2 = 0.27 \text{ g/L}$$

**2.** At 25°C and 1.0 atm, 0.25 g of a gas dissolves in 1.00 L of water. What mass of the gas dissolves in 1.00 L of water at 25°C and 3.0 atm?

$$\frac{S_1}{P_1} = \frac{S_2}{P_2}$$

$$S_2 = S_1\frac{P_2}{P_1} = 0.25 \text{ g/L}\left(\frac{3.0 \text{ atm}}{1.0 \text{ atm}}\right) = 0.75 \text{ g/L}$$

$$S = \frac{m}{V}$$

$$m = SV = (0.75 \text{ g/L})(1.00 \text{ L})$$

$$m = 0.75 \text{ g}$$

**3.** 1.56 g of a gas dissolves in 2.00 L of water at a pressure of 1.75 atm. At what pressure will 2.00 g of the gas dissolve in 2.00 L of water if the temperature remains constant?

$$\frac{S_1}{P_1} = \frac{S_2}{P_2}$$

$$P_2 = P_1\frac{S_2}{S_1} = P_1\frac{m_2/V}{m_1/V} = (1.75 \text{ atm})\left(\frac{2.00 \text{ g}}{1.56 \text{ g}}\right)$$

$$P_2 = 2.24 \text{ atm}$$

**4.** What is the percent by mass of 92.3 g of potassium fluoride (KF) dissolved in 1000.0 g of water?

mass of solution = mass of solute + mass of solvent

mass of solution = 1000.0 g + 92.3 g = 1092.3 g

$$\text{Percent by mass} = \frac{\text{mass of solute}}{\text{mass of solution}} \times 100\%$$

$$= \left(\frac{92.3 \text{ g}}{1092.3 \text{ g}}\right)(100\%)$$

Percent by mass = 8.45%

**5.** A 500.0 g-sample of aqueous hydrogen peroxide ($H_2O_2$) contains 31.50% $H_2O_2$ by mass.

**a.** Find the mass of hydrogen peroxide in the solution.

$$\text{Percent by mass} = \frac{\text{mass of solute}}{\text{mass of solution}} \times 100\%$$

Mass of solute

$$= \frac{\text{percent by mass}}{100\%} \times \text{mass of solution}$$

$$= \left(\frac{31.50\%}{100\%}\right)(500.0 \text{ g})$$

mass of solute = 157.5 g ($H_2O_2$)

**b.** Find the mass of water in the solution.

mass of solution = mass of solute + mass of solvent

mass of solvent = mass of solution − mass of solute

= 500.0 g − 157.5 g

mass of solvent = 342.5 g ($H_2O$)

**6.** If 24.0 mL of methanol ($CH_3OH$) is dissolved in 48.0 mL of water, determine the percent by volume of methanol in the solution.

volume of solution =
volume of solute + volume of solvent

volume of solution = 24.0 mL + 48.0 mL
= 72.0 mL

Percent by volume = $\dfrac{\text{volume of solute}}{\text{volume of solution}} \times 100\%$

= $\left(\dfrac{24.0 \text{ mL}}{72.0 \text{ mL}}\right)(100\%)$

Percent by volume = 33.3%

**7.** An aqueous solution of methanol is 45.0% methanol by volume.

**a.** Find the volume of methanol in a 250.0-mL sample of the solution.

Percent by volume =

$\dfrac{\text{volume of solute}}{\text{volume of solution}} \times 100\%$

Volume of solute =

$\dfrac{\text{percent by volume}}{100\%} \times \text{volume of solution}$

= $\left(\dfrac{45.0\%}{100\%}\right)(250.0 \text{ mL})$

volume of solute = 113 mL (methanol)

**b.** Find the volume of water in this sample of the solution.

volume of solution =
volume of solute + volume of solvent

volume of solvent =
volume of solution − volume of solute

= 250.0 mL − 113 mL

volume of solvent = 137 mL (water)

**8.** What is the molarity of a solution that contains 20.45 g of sodium chloride (NaCl) dissolved in 700.0 mL of solution?

$(20.45 \text{ g NaCl})\left(\dfrac{1 \text{ mol NaCl}}{58.44 \text{ g NaCl}}\right) = 0.3499 \text{ mol NaCl}$

$(700.0 \text{ mL})\left(\dfrac{1 \text{ L}}{1000 \text{ mL}}\right) = 0.7000 \text{ L}$

Molarity = $\dfrac{\text{moles of solute}}{\text{liters of solution}}$

= $\dfrac{0.3499 \text{ mol NaCl}}{0.7000 \text{ L}} = 0.4999 \text{ mol NaCl/L}$

Molarity = 0.5000$M$ NaCl

**9.** Calculate the molarity of 0.205 L of a solution that contains 156.5 g of sucrose ($C_{12}H_{22}O_{11}$).

$(156.5 \text{ g } C_{12}H_{22}O_{11})\left(\dfrac{1 \text{ mol } C_{12}H_{22}O_{11}}{342.34 \text{ g } C_{12}H_{22}O_{11}}\right)$

= 0.4571 mol $C_{12}H_{22}O_{11}$

Molarity = $\dfrac{\text{moles of solute}}{\text{liters of solution}}$

= $\dfrac{0.4571 \text{ mol } C_{12}H_{22}O_{11}}{0.205 \text{ L}} = 2.23 \text{ mol } C_{12}H_{22}O_{11}/L$

Molarity = 2.23$M$ $C_{12}H_{22}O_{11}$

**10.** A 0.600-L sample of a 2.50$M$ solution of potassium iodide (KI) contains what mass of KI?

Molarity = $\dfrac{\text{moles of solute}}{\text{liters of solution}}$

moles of solute = molarity × liters of solution
= (2.50 mol KI/L)(0.600 L)

moles of solute = 1.50 mol KI

$(1.50 \text{ mol KI})\left(\dfrac{1.66 \text{ g KI}}{1 \text{ mol KI}}\right) = 249 \text{ g KI}$

**11.** What mass of ammonium chloride ($NH_4Cl$) would you use to prepare 85.0 mL of a $1.20M$ solution $NH_4Cl$?

$(85.0 \text{ mL})\left(\dfrac{1 \text{ L}}{1000 \text{ mL}}\right) = 0.0850 \text{ L}$

Molarity $= \dfrac{\text{moles of solute}}{\text{liters of solution}}$

moles of solute = molarity × liters of solution
= $(1.20 \text{ mol } NH_4Cl/L)(0.0850 \text{ L})$
moles of solute = 0.102 mol $NH_4Cl$

$(0.102 \text{ mol } NH_4Cl)\left(\dfrac{53.50 \text{ g } NH_4Cl}{1 \text{ mol } NH_4Cl}\right)$

= 5.46 g $NH_4Cl$

**12.** How would you correctly prepare 125 mL of a $0.30M$ solution of copper(II) sulfate ($CuSO_4$) from a $2.00M$ solution of $CuSO_4$?

$M_1V_1 = M_2V_2$

$V_1 = V_2\dfrac{M_2}{M_1} = (125 \text{ mL})\left(\dfrac{0.30M}{2.00M}\right) = 19 \text{ mL}$

Dilute 19 mL $2.00M$ $CuSO_4$ solution to 125 mL with water.

**13.** A 22.0-mL sample of $12M$ $H_2SO_4$ is diluted to a volume of 1200.0 mL. What is the molarity of the diluted solution?

$M_1V_1 = M_2V_2$

$M_2 = M_1\dfrac{V_1}{V_2} = (12M)\left(\dfrac{22.0 \text{ mL}}{1200.0 \text{ mL}}\right)$

= $0.22M$ $H_2SO_4$

**14.** A mass of 134 g of manganese dibromide ($MnBr_2$) is dissolved in 225 g of water. What is the molality of the solution?

$(134 \text{ g } MnBr_2)\left(\dfrac{1 \text{ mol } MnBr_2}{214.74 \text{ g } MnBr_2}\right)$
= 0.624 mol $MnBr_2$

$(225 \text{ g})\left(\dfrac{1 \text{ kg}}{1000 \text{ g}}\right) = 0.225 \text{ kg}$

Molality $= \dfrac{\text{moles of solute}}{\text{kilograms of solvent}}$

$= \dfrac{0.624 \text{ mol } MnBr_2}{0.225 \text{ kg}}$

Molality = $2.77m$ $MnBr_2$

**15.** Calculate the molality of a solution that contains 106 g naphthalene ($C_{10}H_8$) dissolved in 3.15 mol carbon tetrachloride ($CCl_4$).

$(106 \text{ g } C_{10}H_8)\left(\dfrac{1 \text{ mol } C_{10}H_8}{128.18 \text{ g } C_{10}H_8}\right) = 0.827 \text{ mol } C_{10}H_8$

$(3.15 \text{ mol } CCl_4)\left(\dfrac{153.81 \text{ g } CCl_4}{1 \text{ mol } CCl_4}\right) = 485 \text{ g } CCl_4$

$(485 \text{ g})\left(\dfrac{1 \text{ kg}}{1000 \text{ g}}\right) = 0.485 \text{ kg}$

Molality $= \dfrac{\text{moles of solute}}{\text{kilograms of solvent}}$

$= \dfrac{0.827 \text{ mol } C_{10}H_8}{10.485 \text{ kg}}$

Molality = $1.71m$ $C_{10}H_8$

**16.** A solution is made by dissolving 425 g of nitric acid ($HNO_3$) in 535 g of water. Find the mole fraction of nitric acid in the solution.

$(425 \text{ g } HNO_3)\left(\dfrac{1 \text{ mol } HNO_3}{63.02 \text{ g } HNO_3}\right) = 6.74 \text{ mol } HNO_3$

$(535 \text{ g } H_2O)\left(\dfrac{1 \text{ mol } H_2O}{18.02 \text{ g } H_2O}\right) = 29.7 \text{ mol } H_2O$

$X_{HNO_3} = \dfrac{n_{HNO_3}}{n_{HNO_3} + n_{H_2O}} = \dfrac{6.74 \text{ mol}}{6.74 \text{ mol} + 29.7 \text{ mol}}$

$= \dfrac{6.74 \text{ mol}}{36.4 \text{ mol}}$

$X_{HNO_3} = 0.185$

# Chapter 16

1. Calculate the amount of heat released in the complete combustion of 8.17 g of Al to form $Al_2O_3(s)$ at 25°C and 1 atm. $\Delta H_f^\circ$ for $Al_2O_3(s)$ = −1680 kJ/mol.

$$4Al(s) + 3O_2(g) \rightarrow 2Al_2O_3(s)$$

In the reaction, 2 mol $Al_2O_3$ is produced. The enthalpy of formation is −1680 kJ/mol. Therefore, the total energy of this reaction is −3360 kJ. For the combustion of 8.17 g of Al,

8.17 g Al × 1 mol Al/27.0 g Al × (−3360 kJ/4 mol) = −254 kJ.

2. From the following data at 25°C,

$$H_2(g) + Cl_2(g) \rightarrow 2HCl(g) \quad \Delta H = -185 \text{ kJ}$$
$$2H_2(g) + O_2(g) \rightarrow 2H_2O(g) \quad \Delta H = -483.7 \text{ kJ}$$

calculate $\Delta H$ at 25°C for the reaction below.

$$4HCl(g) + O_2(g) \rightarrow 2Cl_2(g) + 2H_2O(g)$$

The final reaction is related to the two reference reactions. According to Hess's law, the final reaction can be obtained by reversing the first reaction and multiplying it by 2, then adding the resulting equation to the second equation. This produces the enthalpy for the final reaction. The result is

2 × (185 kJ) + 1 × (−483.7 kJ) = −114 kJ.

3. Determine $\Delta S$ for the reaction

$$SO_3(g) + H_2O(l) \rightarrow H_2SO_4(l),$$

given the following entropies.

| Compound | Entropy (J/mol·K) |
| --- | --- |
| $SO_3(g)$ | 256.8 |
| $H_2O(l)$ | 70.0 |
| $H_2SO_4(l)$ | 156.9 |

The entropy for the reaction is the entropy of the product minus the entropies of the reactants.

$\Delta S$ = (1 mol $H_2SO_4$ × 156.9 J/mol·K) − (1 mol $SO_3$ × 256.2 J/mol·K) − (1 mol $H_2O$ × 70.0 J/mol·K) = −169.3 J/mol·K

4. Calculate the molar entropy of vaporization for liquid hydrogen iodide at its boiling point, −34.55°C.

$$HI(l) \rightleftharpoons HI(g) \qquad \Delta H_{vap} = 19.76 \text{ kJ/mol}$$

At the boiling point, liquid and gaseous HI exists in equilibrium. Therefore, $\Delta G = 0$.

$\Delta H_{vap}$ = 19.76 kJ/mol

$T = 273 \text{ K} + T_C = 273 \text{ K} + (-34.55°C) = 238 \text{ K}$

$\Delta G = \Delta H - T\Delta S$

$T\Delta S = \Delta H$

$\Delta S = \dfrac{\Delta H}{T} = \dfrac{19.76 \text{ kJ/mol}}{238 \text{ K}} \times \dfrac{1000 \text{ J}}{1 \text{ kJ}}$

= 83.0 J/mol·K

5. Ozone ($O_3$) in the atmosphere may react with nitric oxide (NO).

$$O_3(g) + NO(g) \rightarrow NO_2(g) + O_2(g)$$

From the following data, calculate the $\Delta G^\circ$ in kJ for the reaction at 25°C and determine whether the reaction is spontaneous.

$\Delta H^\circ = -199 \text{ kJ}$

$\Delta S^\circ = -4.1 \text{ J/K}$

$\Delta G = \Delta H - T\Delta S$

$\Delta G = -199 \text{ kJ} - [298 \text{ K} \times (-4.1 \text{ J/K}) \times 1 \text{ kJ/1000 J}]$

$\Delta G = -198 \text{ kJ}$

The reaction is spontaneous.

6. For the reaction $H_2(g) + S(s) \rightarrow H_2S(g)$, $\Delta H = -20.2 \text{ kJ}$ and $\Delta S = 43.1 \text{ J/K}$. When will the reaction be spontaneous?

Spontaneity is determined from the free energy. When the free energy is negative, the reaction will be spontaneous.

$\Delta G = \Delta H - T\Delta S$

The enthalpy is negative and the entropy is positive.

$\Delta G = (-) - (+) = -$

Because the free energy can only be negative, the reaction will be spontaneous at all temperatures.

**7.** The following reaction is nonspontaneous at 25°C.

$$Cu_2O(s) \rightarrow 2Cu(s) + \frac{1}{2}O_2\,(g)$$

$\Delta H_f^\circ = 168.6$ kJ

If $\Delta S = 75.8$ J/K, what is the lowest temperature at which the reaction will be spontaneous?

A reaction is spontaneous when the free energy is negative. When the enthalpy is positive and the entropy is positive, the reaction will be spontaneous at high temperatures. To determine the lowest temperature of spontaneity, determine the temperature of equilibrium. At any temperature higher than that, the reaction will be spontaneous.

$\Delta H = T\Delta S$

$T = \dfrac{\Delta H}{\Delta S} = \dfrac{168.6 \text{ kJ}}{75.8 \text{ J/K}} \times \dfrac{1000 \text{ J}}{1 \text{ kJ}} = 2.22 \times 10^3$ K

**8.** Calculate $\Delta H^\circ$ at 25°C for the reaction below.

$$2ZnS(s) + 3O_2(g) \rightarrow 2ZnO(s) + 2SO_2(g)$$

$\quad -206.0 \qquad 0 \qquad -350.5 \quad -296.8$

$$\Delta H_f^\circ \text{(kJ/mol)}$$

$\Delta H^\circ_{\text{reaction}} = \Sigma\Delta H_f^\circ{}_{\text{products}} - \Sigma\Delta H_f^\circ{}_{\text{reactants}}$

$\Delta H = [2 \text{ mol} \times (-350.5 \text{ kJ/mol}) + 2 \text{ mol} \times (-296.8 \text{ kJ/mol})] - [2 \text{ mol} \times (-206.0 \text{ kJ/mol}) + 3 \text{ mol} \times (0 \text{ kJ/mol})]$

$\Delta H = -882.6$ kJ

**9.** How much heat is evolved in the formation of 35.0 g of $Fe_2O_3(s)$ at 25°C and 1.00 atm pressure by the following reaction?

$$4Fe(s) + 3O_2(g) \rightarrow 2Fe_2O_3(s)$$

$\Delta H_f^\circ$ (kJ/mol) $\quad 0 \qquad 0 \qquad -824.2$

The formation of one mole of iron(III) oxide releases −824.2 kJ.

$35.0 \text{ g } Fe_2O_3 \times 1 \text{ mol } Fe_2O_3/159.7 \text{ g } Fe_2O_3 \times (-824.2 \text{ kJ}/1 \text{ mol } Fe_2O_3) = -181$ kJ

**10.** Calculate the standard heat of vaporization, $\Delta H_{\text{vap}}$, for tin(IV) chloride, $SnCl_4$.

$\Delta H_f^\circ = -511.3$ kJ/mol for $SnCl_4(l)$ and $-471.5$ kJ/mol for $SnCl_4(g)$.

At the boiling point, $SnCl_4(l) \rightleftharpoons SnCl_4(g)$.

$\Delta H_{\text{vap}} = \Sigma H_f^\circ{}_{\text{products}} - \Sigma H_f^\circ{}_{\text{reactants}}$

$\Delta H_{\text{vap}} = [1 \text{ mol} \times (-471.5 \text{ kJ/mol})] - [1 \text{ mol} \times (-511.3 \text{ kJ/mol})]$

$\Delta H_{\text{vap}} = 39.8$ kJ

**11.** Given the following data at 298 K, calculate $\Delta S$ for the given reaction.

$$2Ag_2O(s) \rightarrow 4Ag(s) + O_2(g)$$

$\Delta S$ (J/mol·K) $\quad 121.3 \qquad 42.6 \qquad 205.2$

$\Delta S_{\text{reaction}} = \Sigma\Delta S_{\text{products}} - \Sigma\Delta S_{\text{reactants}}$

$\Delta S_{\text{reaction}} = [4 \text{ mol} \times 42.6 \text{ J/mol·K} + 1 \text{ mol} \times 205.2 \text{ J/mol·K}] - [2 \text{ mol} \times 121.3 \text{ J/mol·K}]$

$\Delta S_{\text{reaction}} = 133.0$ J/K

**12.** Calculate the $\Delta G^\circ$ at 298 K for the following reaction.

$$Fe_2O_3(s) + 13CO(g) \rightarrow 2Fe(CO)_5(g) + 3CO_2(g)$$

$\quad -824.2 \quad -110.5 \qquad -733.8 \qquad -393.5$

$$\Delta H^\circ \text{ (kJ/mol)}$$

$\quad 87.4 \qquad 197.6 \qquad\quad 445.2 \qquad\quad 213.6$

$$\Delta S^\circ \text{ (J/mol·K)}$$

$\Delta G^\circ_{\text{reaction}} = \Delta H^\circ_{\text{reaction}} - T\Delta S^\circ_{\text{reaction}}$

$\Delta H^\circ_{\text{reaction}} = \Sigma\Delta H^\circ_{\text{products}} - \Sigma\Delta H^\circ_{\text{reactants}}$

$\Delta S^\circ_{\text{reaction}} = \Sigma\Delta S^\circ_{\text{products}} - \Sigma\Delta S^\circ_{\text{reactants}}$

$\Delta H^\circ_{\text{reaction}} = [2 \text{ mol} \times (-733.8 \text{ kJ/mol}) + 3 \text{ mol} \times (-393.5 \text{ kJ/mol})] - [1 \text{ mol} \times (-824.2 \text{ kJ/mol}) + 13 \text{ mol} \times (-110.5 \text{ kJ/mol})] = -387.4$ kJ

$\Delta S^\circ_{\text{reaction}} = [2 \text{ mol} \times (445.2 \text{ J/mol·K}) + 3 \text{ mol} \times (213.6 \text{ J/mol·K})] - [1 \text{ mol} \times (87.4 \text{ J/mol·K}) + 13 \text{ mol} \times (197.6 \text{ J/mol·K})] = -1125$ J/K

$\Delta G_{\text{reaction}} = -387.4 \text{ kJ} - (298 \text{ K} \times (-1125 \text{ J/K}) \times 1 \text{ kJ}/1000 \text{ J})$

$\Delta G_{\text{reaction}} = -52.2$ kJ

**13.** Estimate the temperature at which $\Delta G = 0$ for the following reaction.

$NH_3(g) + HCl(g) \rightarrow NH_4Cl(s)$

$\Delta H = -176$ kJ, $\Delta S = -284.5$ J/K

$\Delta G = \Delta H - T\Delta S$     At equilibrium, $\Delta G = 0$.

$\Delta H = T\Delta S$

$T = \Delta H/\Delta S$

$T = -176 \text{ kJ}/(-284.5 \text{ J/K} \times 1\text{ kJ}/1000 \text{ J}) = 619$ K or 346°C

**14.** Consider the reaction below at 25°C for which $\Delta S = 16.1$ J/K.

$CH_4(g) + N_2(g) + 163.8 \text{ kJ} \rightarrow$
$HCN(g) + NH_3(g)$

At what temperature will this reaction be spontaneous?

$\Delta G = 0$ at equilibrium. $\Delta G =$ negative value for spontaneous reaction.

Find the temperature of equilibrium. The reaction is spontaneous at any temperature higher than equilibrium temperature.

$\Delta G = \Delta H - T\Delta S$     at $\Delta G = 0$, $\Delta H = T\Delta S$.

$T = 163.8 \text{ kJ}/(16.1 \text{ J/K} \times 1\text{ kJ}/1000 \text{ J}) = 1.02 \times 10^4$ K $= 9.90 \times 10^3$°C

Spontaneity occurs at any temperature higher than $9.90 \times 10^3$°C.

**15.** Estimate the temperature above which the following reaction is not spontaneous.

$PbS(s) + 2HCl(g) \rightarrow PbCl_2(s) + H_2S(g)$
$\quad -100.4 \quad -92.31 \quad\quad -359.4 \quad -20.60$
$\quad\quad\quad\quad \Delta H_f^\circ \text{ (kJ/mol)}$

$\quad -98.70 \quad -95.30 \quad\quad -314.1 \quad -33.60$
$\quad\quad\quad\quad \Delta G^\circ \text{ (kJ/mol)}$

To determine the temperature of spontaneity, the enthalpy and entropy values must be known. Get the entropy values from the free energy and the enthalpy at the standard state (T = 298 K).

$\Delta G_{reaction} = \Sigma\Delta G_{products} - \Sigma\Delta G_{reactants}$
$\Delta G_{reaction} = [1 \text{ mol} \times (-314.1 \text{ kJ/mol}) + 1 \text{ mol} \times (-33.60 \text{ kJ/mol})] - [1 \text{ mol} \times (-98.70 \text{ kJ/mol}) + 2 \text{ mol} \times (-95.30 \text{ kJ/mol})] = -58.4$ kJ

$\Delta H_{reaction} = \Delta H_{products} - \Delta H_{reactants}$
$\Delta H^\circ_{reaction} = [1 \text{ mol} \times (-359.4 \text{ kJ/mol}) + 1 \text{ mol} \times (-20.60 \text{ kJ/mol})] - [1 \text{ mol} \times (-100.4 \text{ kJ/mol}) + 2 \text{ mol} \times (-92.31 \text{ kJ/mol})] = -94.98$ kJ

$\Delta S = (\Delta H - \Delta G)/T$

$\Delta S = (-94.98 \text{ kJ} - (-58.4 \text{ kJ}))/298 \text{ K} = -0.123$ kJ/K

$-0.123 \text{ kJ/K} \times \dfrac{1000 \text{ J}}{1 \text{ kJ}} = -123$ J/K

Equilibrium occurs when the free energy is zero.

$T = \Delta H/\Delta S$

$T = -94.98 \text{ kJ}/(-123 \text{ J/K} \times 1 \text{ kJ}/1000 \text{ J}) = 772$ K $= 449$°C

The reaction is not spontaneous above this temperature.

**16.** Copper metal has a specific heat of 0.385 J/g·°C and a melting point of 1083°C. Calculate the amount of heat required to raise the temperature of 22.8 g of copper from 20.0°C to 875°C.

$q = c \times m \times \Delta T$
$q = 0.385 \text{ J/g·°C} \times 22.8 \text{ g} \times (875°C - 20.0°C) \times \dfrac{1 \text{ kJ}}{1000 \text{ J}} = 7.51$ kJ

**17.** How many degrees of temperature rise will occur when a 25.0-g block of aluminum absorbs 10.0 kJ of heat? The specific heat of aluminum is 0.897 J/g·°C.

$q = c \times m \times \Delta T$
$\Delta T = \dfrac{q}{c \times m}$
$(T_{final} - T_{initial}) = 10\,000 \text{ J}/(25.0 \text{ g} \times 0.897 \text{ J/g·°C}) = 446$°C

**18.** Find the standard enthalpy of formation for ethylene, $C_2H_4(g)$, given the following data.

$C_2H_4(g) + 3O_2(g) \rightarrow 2CO_2(g) + 2H_2O(l)$

$\Delta H° = -1411$ kJ

$C(s) + O_2(g) \rightarrow CO_2(g)$

$\Delta H° = -393.5$ kJ

$H_2(g) + \frac{1}{2}O_2(g) \rightarrow H_2O(l)$

$\Delta H° = -285.8$ kJ

Use Hess's law and rearrange the equations to get the equation for the formation of ethylene from elemental carbon and hydrogen. Multiply by the appropriate coefficients.

$2CO_2(g) + 2H_2O(l) \rightarrow C_2H_4(g) + 3O_2(g)$

$\Delta H° = 1411$ kJ

$2C(s) + 2O_2(g) \rightarrow 2CO_2(g)$

$\Delta H° = -787.0$ kJ

$2H_2(g) + O_2(g) \rightarrow 2H_2O(l)$

$\Delta H° = -571.6$ kJ

Then add the enthalpies to get the enthalpy of formation for

$2C(s) + 2H_2(g) \rightarrow C_2H_4(g) \qquad \Delta H = 52.4$ kJ

**19.** Glycine is important for biological energy. The combustion of glycine is given by the following equation.

$4C_2H_5O_2N(s) + 9O_2(g) \rightarrow$
$\quad 8CO_2(g) + 10H_2O(l) + 2N_2(g)$

$\Delta H = -3857$ kJ

Given that $\Delta H_f° \; CO_2(g) = -393.5$ kJ/mol and $\Delta H_f° \; H_2O(l) = -285.8$ kJ/mol, calculate the enthalpy of formation per mole of glycine.

$\Delta H°_{reaction} = \Sigma\Delta H°_{products} - \Sigma\Delta H°_{reactants}$

$-3857$ kJ = [8 mol $\times$ ($-393.5$ kJ/mol) + 10 mol $\times$ ($-285.8$ kJ/mol) + 2 mol $\times$ 0 kJ/mol] $-$ [4 mol $\times$ ($\Delta H$ glycine) + 9 mol $\times$ 0 kJ/mol]

$\Delta H$ glycine = ($-3857$ kJ + 3148 kJ + 2858 kJ)/ $-4$ mol = $-537.3$ kJ/mol

**20.** At body temperature, 2404 J is required to evaporate 1 g of water. After vigorous exercise, a person feels chilly because the body is giving up heat to evaporate the perspiration. A typical person perspires 25 mL of water after 20 minutes of exercise. How much body heat is used to evaporate this water?

Convert the 25 mL of water to grams of water.

25 mL $\times$ 1 g/1 mL = 25 g

25 g $\times$ 2404 J/g $\times \dfrac{1kJ}{1000 \, J}$ = 60 kJ

# Chapter 17

**1.** For the reaction $BrO_3^- + 5Br^- + 6H^+ \rightarrow 3Br_2 + 3H_2O$, the value of $\dfrac{-\Delta[BrO_3^-]}{\Delta t} =$ $1.5 \times 10^{-2}$ mol/(L·s) at a particular time. What is the value of $\dfrac{-\Delta[Br^-]}{\Delta t}$ at the same instant?

$1.5 \times 10^{-2}$ mol/(L·s) = $\dfrac{\Delta[BrO_3^-]}{\Delta t}$ =
$(1/5)\left(\dfrac{-\Delta[Br^-]}{\Delta t}\right)$

$(1.5 \times 10^{-2}$ mol/(L·s)$) \times 5 = \dfrac{-\Delta[Br^-]}{\Delta t}$

$7.5 \times 10^{-2}$ mol/(L·s) = $\dfrac{-\Delta[Br^-]}{\Delta t}$

**2.** The reaction, A + 2B $\rightarrow$ Products, was found to have the rate law, Rate = $k[A][B]^2$. While holding the concentration of A constant, the concentration of B was increased from $x$ to $3x$. Predict by what factor the rate of the reaction will increase.

Let $x$ = [B] and $y$ = [A] initially.

Initial rate = $k[A][B]^2 = k(y)(x)^2$

[A] does not change but [B] triples.

Increased rate = $k(y)(3x)^2 = k(y)(x)^2(3)^2$
= 9 (initial rate)

The rate of reaction will increase by a factor of 9.

**3.** For the hypothetical reaction A + B → Products, the following initial rates of reaction have been measured for the given reactant concentrations.

| Test | [A] ($M$) | [B] ($M$) | Rate (mol/(L·hr)) |
|------|-----------|-----------|-------------------|
| 1 | 0.010 | 0.020 | 0.020 |
| 2 | 0.015 | 0.020 | 0.030 |
| 3 | 0.010 | 0.010 | 0.005 |

What is the rate law expression for this reaction?

Set up the rate equation for all three tests.

Rate 1 = $k[0.010]^m[0.020]^n$

Rate 2 = $k[0.015]^m[0.020]^n$ = $k(1.5)^m[0.010]^m[0.020]^n$ = $(1.5)^m$(Rate 1)

Rate 3 = $k[0.010]^m[0.010]^n$ = $k[0.010]^m(0.5)^n[0.020]^n$ = $(0.5)^n$(Rate 1)

$\frac{\text{(Rate 2)}}{\text{(Rate 1)}} = (1.5)^m$

$\frac{0.030}{0.020} = (1.5)^m$

$1.5 = (1.5)^m$

$m = 1$

$\frac{\text{(Rate 3)}}{\text{(Rate 1)}} = (0.5)^n$

$\frac{0.005}{0.020} = (0.5)^n$

$0.25 = (0.5)^n$

$n = 2$

Substitute $m$ and $n$ to get Rate = $k[A]^1[B]^2$.

**4.** For the chemical reaction $H_2O_2 + 2H^+ + 2I^- \rightarrow I_2 + 2H_2O$, the rate law expression is Rate = $k[H_2O_2][I^-]$. The following mechanism has been suggested.

$$H_2O_2 + I^- \rightarrow HOI + OH^-$$

$$OH^- + H+ \rightarrow H_2O$$

$$HOI + H^+ + I^- \rightarrow I_2 + H_2O$$

Identify all intermediates included in this reaction.

The intermediates are $OH^-$ and HOI.

**5.** Consider the following rate data for the reaction below at a particular temperature.

$$2A + 3B \rightarrow \text{Products}$$

| Experiment | Initial [A] ($M$) | Initial [B] ($M$) | Initial Rate of Loss of A (mol/(L·s)) |
|------------|-------------------|-------------------|----------------------------------------|
| 1 | 0.10 | 0.30 | $1.00 \times 10^{-5}$ |
| 2 | 0.10 | 0.60 | $2.00 \times 10^{-5}$ |
| 3 | 0.20 | 0.90 | $1.20 \times 10^{-4}$ |

What is the rate equation for this reaction?

Rate 1 = $k[0.10]^m[0.30]^n$

Rate 2 = $k[0.10]^m[0.60]^n = k[0.10]^m[0.30]^n(2)^n$ = $(2)^n$(Rate 1)

Rate 3 = $k[0.20]^m[0.90]^n = k[0.10]^m(2)^m[0.30]^n(3)^n$ = $(2)^m(3)^n$(Rate 1)

$(2)^n = \frac{\text{(Rate 2)}}{\text{(Rate 1)}} = \frac{(2.00 \times 10^{-5}\ \text{mol/(L·s)})}{(1.00 \times 10^{-5}\ \text{mol/(L·s)})} = 2$

$n = 1$

$(2)^m(3)^n = \frac{\text{(Rate 3)}}{\text{(Rate 1)}} = \frac{(1.20 \times 10^{-4}\ \text{mol/(L·s)})}{(1.00 \times 10^{-5}\ \text{mol/(L·s)})} = 12$

$(2)^m(3)^1 = 12$

$(2)^m = 4$

$m = 2$

Rate = $k[A]^2[B]^1$

**6.** Consider a chemical reaction involving compounds A and B that is found to be first order in A and second order in B. What will the reaction rate be for experiment 2?

| Experiment | Rate (mol/(L·s)) | Initial [A] ($M$) | Initial [B] ($M$) |
|------------|------------------|-------------------|-------------------|
| 1 | 0.10 | 1.0 | 0.2 |
| 2 | ? | 2.0 | 0.6 |

Rate 1 = 0.10 mol/(L·s) = $k[1.0]^1[0.2]^2$ = $k(1.0)(0.04)$

$k = 2.5$ L mol$^{-1}$ s$^{-1}$

Rate 2 = 2.5 L mol$^{-1}$ s$^{-1}[2.0]^1[0.6]^2$ = 1.8 mol/(L·s)

**7.** The data below were determined for the following reaction.

$$S_2O_8{}^{2-} + 3I^- \rightarrow 2SO_4{}^{2-} + I_3$$

| Experiment | $[S_2O_8{}^{2-}]$ (M) | $I^-$ (M) | Initial Rate (mol/(L·s)) |
|---|---|---|---|
| 1 | 0.10 | 0.40 | $1.4 \times 10^{-5}$ |
| 2 | 0.20 | 0.40 | $2.8 \times 10^{-5}$ |
| 3 | 0.20 | 0.20 | $1.4 \times 10^{-5}$ |

What is the rate equation for this reaction?

Rate 1 = $k[0.10]^m[0.40]^n$

Rate 2 = $k[0.20]^m[0.40]^n = k[0.10]^m(2)^m[0.40]^n$
$\qquad = (2)^m$(Rate 1)

Rate 3 = $k[0.20]^m[0.20]^n =$
$\qquad k[0.10]^m(2)^m[0.40]^n(0.5)^n =$
$\qquad (2)^m(0.5)^n$(Rate 1)

$(2)^m = \dfrac{\text{(Rate 2)}}{\text{(Rate 1)}} = \dfrac{(2.8 \times 10^{-5}\ \text{mol/(L·s)})}{(1.4 \times 10^{-5}\ \text{mol/(L·s)})} = 2$

$m = 1$

$(2)^m(0.5)^n = 2(0.5)^n = \dfrac{\text{(Rate 3)}}{\text{(Rate 1)}} =$

$\dfrac{(1.4 \times 10^{-5}\ \text{mol/(L·s)})}{(1.4 \times 10^{-5})} = 1$

$(0.5)^n = 0.5$

$n = 1$

Rate = $k[S_2O_8{}^{2-}][I^-]$

**8.** For the reaction $A + B \rightarrow C$, the rate relationship is found to be Rate = $k[A][B]^2$. What is the overall reaction order for this reaction?

The reaction is first order in A and second order in B. (1 + 2 = 3)

This is a third-order reaction.

**9.** For the rate law expression Rate = $k[A][B]^2$, what happens to the rate if the concentration of B is increased by a factor of 2?

The rate will increase by a factor of 4. $(2)^2 = 4$

**10.** Calculate the specific rate constant for the reaction $A + B \rightarrow C$, when the rate expression is Rate = $k[A]^2[B]$.

| Experiment | Initial [A] (M) | Initial [B] (M) | Initial Rate of Formation of C (mol/(L·s)) |
|---|---|---|---|
| 1 | 0.10 | 0.10 | $2.0 \times 10^{-4}$ |
| 2 | 0.20 | 0.10 | $8.0 \times 10^{-4}$ |
| 3 | 0.20 | 0.20 | $1.6 \times 10^{-3}$ |

$2.0 \times 10^{-4}\ \text{mol/(L·s)} = k[0.10]^2[0.10]$
$k = 0.20\ \text{L}^2\,\text{mol}^{-2}\,\text{s}^{-1} = 2.0 \times 10^{-1}\ \text{L}^2\,\text{mol}^{-2}\,\text{s}^{-1}$

**11.** The following figure shows the energy diagram of some reactants changing into products. Explain what the numbers in the diagram represent.

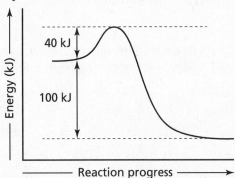

The reaction has an activation energy of 40 kJ and an overall energy change of reaction of $-100$ kJ. This reaction will be exothermic with a loss of 100 kJ energy.

**12.** The following figure shows the potential energy diagram for a reaction. Explain what this diagram tells you about the reaction.

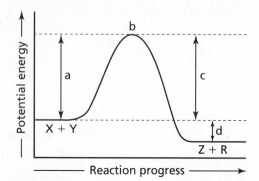

The reaction can be expressed as X + Y → Z + R. The forward reaction has an activation energy of **a**. The reverse reaction has an activation energy of **c** + **d**. Intermediate **b** is formed during the rate-determining step. The reaction releases energy **d**. The reaction is exothermic.

**13.** Explain how the following mechanism can be used to determine the rate expression for a chemical reaction A + 2B → AB$_2$.

| Step 1 | B + B → B$_2$ | slow |
| Step 2 | B$_2$ + A → AB + B | fast |
| Step 3 | B + AB → AB$_2$ | fast |

The slow step is the rate-determining step and is responsible for the rate. Two units of B are involved, so the reaction will be second order in B. The rate expression is then Rate = $k$[B]$^2$. The overall reaction order for this reaction is second order.

**14.** What is the rate law expression for the following mechanism?

| Step 1 | AB + C$_2$ → AC$_2$ + B | slow |
| Step 2 | B + AB → AB$_2$ | fast |
| Step 3 | AC$_2$ + AB$_2$ → A$_2$C$_2$ + B$_2$ | fast |
| Step 4 | A$_2$C$_2$ + B$_2$ → A$_2$C + B$_2$C | fast |

Use the slow step, which is rate determining. Rate = $k$[AB][C$_2$]

# Chapter 18

**1.** Write equilibrium expressions for the following reactions.

**a.** $NH_4HS(g) \rightleftharpoons NH_3(g) + H_2S(g)$

$$K_{eq} = \frac{[NH_3][H_2S]}{[NH_4HS]}$$

**b.** $4HCl(g) + O_2(g) \rightleftharpoons 2Cl_2(g) + 2H_2O(g)$

$$K_{eq} = \frac{[Cl_2]^2[H_2O]^2}{[HCl]^4[O_2]}$$

**c.** $PCl_5(g) \rightleftharpoons PCl_3(g) + Cl_2(g)$

$$K_{eq} = \frac{[Cl_2][PCl_3]}{[PCl_5]}$$

**d.** $CuSO_4 \cdot 3H_2O(s) + 2H_2O(g) \rightleftharpoons CuSO_4 \cdot 5H_2O(s)$

$$K_{eq} = \frac{1}{[H_2O]^2}$$

**2.** At 793 K, the equilibrium constant for the reaction $NCl_3(g) + Cl_2(g) \rightleftharpoons NCl_5(g)$ is 39.3.

**a.** Do products or reactants dominate in this equilibrium?

Products dominate in this equilibrium.

**b.** If the equilibrium constant for this reaction were less than 1, would the reactants or products be dominant?

When the equilibrium constant is less than 1, the reactants are dominant.

**3.** At 773 K, the reaction $2NO(g) + O_2(g) \rightleftharpoons 2NO_2(g)$ produces the following concentrations: [NO] = $3.49 \times 10^{-4}M$; [O$_2$] = 0.80$M$; [NO$_2$] = 0.25$M$.

**a.** What is the equilibrium constant expression for the reaction?

$$K_{eq} = \frac{[NO_2]^2}{[NO]^2[O_2]}$$

**b.** What is the equilibrium constant for the reaction?

$$K_{eq} = 6.4 \times 10^5$$

Solution:
Substituting the equilibrium values into the expression and solving gives the $K_{eq}$.

$$K_{eq} = \frac{[0.25]^2}{[3.49 \times 10^{-4}]^2[0.80]} = 6.4 \times 10^5$$

**4.** If you wished to maximize the products of the following reactions, which concentrations would you lower or raise?

**a.** $H_2(g) + Br_2(g) \rightleftharpoons 2HBr(g)$

Add $H_2$ or $Br_2$, or remove HBr as it is formed.

**b.** $CO_2(g) + H_2(g) \rightleftharpoons CO(g) + H_2O(g)$

Add $CO_2$ or $H_2$, or remove CO or $H_2O$ as they are formed.

**c.** $SO_2(g) + NO_2(g) \rightleftharpoons SO_3(g) + NO(g)$

Add $SO_2$ or $NO_2$, or remove $SO_3$ or NO as they are formed.

**d.** $C(s) + CO_2(g) \rightleftharpoons 2CO(g)$

Raise the concentration of $CO_2(g)$, or lower the concentration of CO(g).

**5.** For each reaction, state whether increasing or decreasing the volume of the reaction vessel would yield more product at equilibrium. Give the reason for your choice.

**a.** $N_2O_4(g) \rightleftharpoons 2NO_2(g)$

Increase the volume to increase $NO_2$ production. This decreases the pressure and so favors the reaction in which more moles are formed.

**b.** $2SO_3(g) \rightleftharpoons 2SO_2(g) + O_2(g)$

Increase the volume to increase $SO_2$ and $O_2$ production. This decreases the pressure and so favors the reaction in which more moles are formed.

**c.** $CH_4(g) + 2O_2(g) \rightleftharpoons CO_2(g) + 2H_2O(g)$

Because the same number of moles are on both sides of the reaction, increasing or decreasing the volume of the reaction vessel has no effect on the product yield.

**d.** $2CO(g) + O_2(g) \rightleftharpoons 2CO_2(g)$

Decrease the volume to increase $CO_2$ production. This forces the equilibrium to the side with the fewer number of moles. There are fewer moles of products than of reactants.

**6.** What effect would an increase in temperature have on these reactions at equilibrium? Why?

**a.** Heat $+ H_2(g) + I_2(g) \rightleftharpoons 2HI(g)$

Temperature increase favors the forward reaction. The reaction that moves to the right consumes heat and so would relieve this stress.

**b.** $CH_4(g) + 2O_2(g) \rightleftharpoons CO(g) + 2H_2O + $ heat

Temperature increase favors the reverse reaction. The reaction that moves to the left consumes heat and so would relieve this stress.

**c.** $N_2(g) + 3H_2(g) \rightleftharpoons 2NH_3(g) + $ heat

Temperature increase favors the reverse reaction. The reaction that moves to the left consumes heat and so would relieve this stress.

**d.** Heat $+ CH_4(g) \rightleftharpoons C(s) + 2H_2(g)$

Temperature increase favors the forward reaction. The reaction that moves to the right consumes heat and so would relieve this stress.

**7.** Phosphorous pentachloride decomposes to phosphorous trichloride according to this equation: $PCl_5(g) \rightleftharpoons PCl_3(g) + Cl_2(g)$. At equilibrium, $[PCl_5] = 1.00M$ and $[Cl_2] = 3.16 \times 10^{-2}M$.

**a.** Write the expression for determining the concentration of $PCl_3$.

$$[PCl_3] = K_{eq} \times \frac{[PCl_5]}{[Cl_2]}$$

Solution:

$$K_{eq} = \frac{[PCl_3][Cl_2]}{[PCl_5]}; \text{ solving for } [PCl_3] \text{ gives}$$

$$[PCl_3] = K_{eq} \times \frac{[PCl_5]}{[Cl_2]}$$

**b.** What is the equilibrium concentration of $PCl_3$? Use: $K_{eq} = 1.00 \times 10^{-3}$.

Answer: $[PCl_3] = 3.16 \times 10^{-2}M$

Solution:

Substitute known concentrations and calculate $[PCl_3]$.

$$[PCl_3] = (1.00 \times 10^{-3}) \times \frac{(1.00)}{(3.16 \times 10^{-2})}$$

$$= 3.16 \times 10^{-2}M$$

**8.** The solubility product constant ($K_{sp}$) of $Ag_2SO_4$ is $1.2 \times 10^{-5}$.

**a.** How would you estimate the molar solubility of $SO_4^{2-}$ without actually calculating it?

Answer: Write the solubility equilibrium equation and the solubility product expression for $Ag_2SO_4$.

$$Ag_2SO_4(s) \rightleftharpoons 2Ag^+(aq) + SO_4^{2-}(aq)$$

$$K_{sp} = [Ag^+]^2[SO_4^{2-}] = 1.2 \times 10^{-5}$$

$K_{sp}$ is about $10^{-5}$; the estimate would be the cube root or about $10^{-1}$ to $10^{-2}$.

**b.** What is the calculated molar solubility of $SO_4^{2-}$?

Answer: Solubility = $[SO_4^{2-}] = 1.4 \times 10^{-2}$

Solution:

There are two $Ag^+$ ions for every $SO_4^{2-}$ ion. Let $s$ equal $[SO_4^{2-}]$; $[Ag^+] = 2s$.

Substitute these terms into the $K_{sp}$ expression and solve for $s$.

$$(2s)^2(s) = 4s^3 = 1.2 \times 10^{-5}$$

$$s^3 = 3.0 \times 10^{-6}$$

Take the cube root of both sides.

$s = 1.4 \times 10^{-2} = [SO_4^{2-}]$. (This is in good agreement with the estimate.)

# Chapter 19

**Write balanced chemical equations for each of the following reactions that involve acids and bases.**

**1.** aluminum and hydrochloric acid

$$2Al(s) + 6HCl(aq) \rightarrow 2AlCl_3(aq) + 3H_2(g)$$

**2.** nitric acid and sodium carbonate

$$2HNO_3(aq) + Na_2CO_3(s) \rightarrow$$
$$2NaNO_3(aq) + H_2O(l) + CO_2(g)$$

**3.** potassium hydroxide and sulfuric acid

$$2KOH(aq) + H_2SO_4(aq) \rightarrow K_2SO_4(aq) + 2H_2O(l)$$

**Write the steps in the complete ionization of the following polyprotic acids.**

**4.** $H_2CO_3$

$$H_2CO_3(aq) + H_2O(l) \rightleftharpoons H_3O^+(aq) + HCO_3^-(aq);$$
$$HCO_3^-(aq) + H_2O(l) \rightleftharpoons H_3O^+(aq) + CO_3^{2-}(aq)$$

**5.** $H_3BO_3$

$H_3BO_3(aq) + H_2O(l) \rightleftharpoons H_3O^+(aq) + H_2BO_3^-(aq);$
$H_2BO_3^-(aq) + H_2O(l) \rightleftharpoons H_3O^+(aq) + HBO_3^{2-}(aq);$
$HBO_3^{2-}(aq) + H_2O(l) \rightleftharpoons H_3O^+(aq) + BO_3^{3-}(aq)$

A solution has a $[H^+]$ of $1.0 \times 10^{-5}M$.

**6.** What is its $[OH^-]$?

$\dfrac{1.0 \times 10^{-14}}{1.0 \times 10^{-5}} = 1.0 \times 10^{-9}M$

**7.** What is its pH?

$-\log(1.0 \times 10^{-5}) = 5$

**8.** What is its pOH?

$14 - 5 = 9$

A solution has a $[OH^-]$ of $3.6 \times 10^{-7}M$.

**9.** What is its $[H^+]$?

$\dfrac{1.0 \times 10^{-14}}{3.6 \times 10^{-7}} = 2.8 \times 10^{-8}M$

**10.** What is its pH?

$-\log(2.8 \times 10^{-8}) = 7.56$

**11.** What is its pOH?

$14.00 - 7.56 = 6.44$

A solution has a $[H^+]$ of $5.6 \times 10^{-6}M$.

**12.** What is its $[OH^-]$?

$\dfrac{1.0 \times 10^{-14}}{5.6 \times 10^{-6}} = 1.8 \times 10^{-9}M$

**13.** What is its pH?

$-\log(5.6 \times 10^{-6}) = 5.25$

**14.** What is its pOH?

$14.0 - 5.25 = 8.75$

A solution has a pH of 5.79.

**15.** What is its pOH?

$14.00 - 5.79 = 8.21$

**16.** What is its $[H^+]$?

$antilog(-5.79) = 1.6 \times 10^{-6}M$

**17.** What is its $[OH-]$?

$\dfrac{1.0 \times 10^{-14}}{1.6 \times 10^{-6}} = 6.3 \times 10^{-9}M$

**18.** What is the pH of a $0.50M$ solution of HCl, a strong acid?

$pH = -\log 0.50 = 0.30$

**19.** What is the pH of a $1.5 \times 10^{-3}M$ solution of NaOH, a strong base?

$[H^+] = \dfrac{1.00 \times 10^{-14}}{1.5 \times 10^{-3}} = 6.7 \times 10^{-12}M;\ pH$

$= -\log (6.7 \times 10^{-12}) = 11.17$

**20.** What is the molarity of a KOH solution if 25.0 mL of it is neutralized by 31.7 mL of a $0.100M$ nitric acid solution?

$KOH(aq) + HNO_3(aq) \rightarrow KNO_3(aq) + H_2O(l);$
0.0317 L̶ ̶H̶N̶O̶₃ $\times$ 0.100 mol $HNO_3$/L̶ ̶H̶N̶O̶₃
$= 3.17 \times 10^{-3}$ mol $HNO_3$;
mol $HNO_3$ : mol KOH = 1:1,
so $3.17 \times 10^{-3}$ mol $HNO_3$ : $3.17 \times 10^{-3}$ mol KOH;
$3.17 \times 10^{-3}$ mol KOH/0.0250 L KOH = $0.127M$

**21.** During a titration, 0.200$M$ HCl is added to a NaOH solution of unknown concentration. What is the concentration of the NaOH solution if 20.0 mL of it is neutralized by 30.7 mL of the standard solution?

NaOH(aq) + HCl(aq) → NaCl(aq) + $H_2O$(l);
0.0307 L HCl × 0.200 mol HCl/L HCl
= 6.14 × $10^{-3}$ mol HCl;
mol HCl : mol NaOH = 1:1,
so 6.14 × $10^{-3}$ mol HCl : 6.14 × $10^{-3}$ mol NaOH;
6.14 × $10^{-3}$ mol NaOH/0.0200 L NaOH = 0.307$M$

**22.** A 25.0-mL sample of $H_2SO_4$ is neutralized by 27.4 mL of 1.00$M$ KOH. What is the concentration of the acid?

2KOH(aq) + $H_2SO_4$(aq) → $K_2SO_4$ (aq) + $2H_2O$(l);
0.0274 L KOH × 1.00 mol KOH/L KOH
= 0.0274 mol KOH; mol KOH : mol $H_2SO_4$ = 2:1,
so 0.0274 mol KOH : 0.0137 mol $H_2SO_4$;
0.0137 mol $H_2SO_4$/0.0250 L $H_2SO_4$ = 0.548$M$

**23.** A 50.0-mL sample of 0.0100$M$ $Ca(OH)_2$ is neutralized by 45.6 mL of HBr. What is the molarity of the acid?

$Ca(OH)_2$(aq) + 2HBr(aq) → $CaBr_2$(aq) + $2H_2O$(l);
0.0500 L $Ca(OH)_2$ × 0.0100 mol $Ca(OH)_2$/L $Ca(OH)_2$
= 5.00 × $10^{-4}$ mol $Ca(OH)_2$;
mol $Ca(OH)_2$ : mol HBr = 1:2,
so 5.00 × $10^{-4}$ mol $Ca(OH)_2$ : 1.00 × $10^{-3}$ mol HBr;
1.00 × $10^{-3}$ mol HBr/0.0456 L HBr = 0.0219$M$

# Chapter 20

**Determine the oxidation number of the boldface element in these ions.**

**1.** $HgCl_4^-$

+3

**2.** $NO_2$

+4

**3.** $MnO_2$

+4

**4.** metallic **Au**

0

**5.** $Na_2SiF_6$

+4

**6.** $Zn(NO_3)_2$

+5

**7.** $Mg_3P_2$

−3

**8.** $Na_3PO_4$

+5

**9.** $H_2O_2$

−1

**10.** $ClO_3^-$

+5

**Balance the following equations, using the oxidation number method for the redox part of the equation. Show your work.**

**11.** $Cu_2O$(s) + $H_2$(g) → Cu(s) + $H_2O$(l)

2(−1) = −2
$Cu_2O$(s) + $H_2$(g) → 2Cu(s) + $H_2O$(l)
2(+1) = +2

$Cu_2O$(s) + $H_2$(g) → 2Cu(s) + $H_2O$(l)

**12.** $Cl_2(g) + KBr(aq) \rightarrow Br_2(l) + KCl(aq)$

$$\overset{-1}{\vphantom{|}}$$

$Cl_2(g) + KBr(aq) \rightarrow Br_2(l) + KCl(aq)$

$$\overset{+1}{\vphantom{|}}$$

$Cl_2(g) + 2KBr(aq) \rightarrow Br_2(l) + 2KCl(aq)$

**13.** $CaSi_2(s) + SbCl_3(s) \rightarrow$
 $Sb(s) + Si(s) + CaCl_2(s)$

$$3(+1) = +3$$

$CaSi_2(s) + SbCl_3(s) \rightarrow Sb(s) + Si(s) + CaCl_2(s)$

$$-3$$

$3CaSi_2(s) + 2SbCl_3(s) \rightarrow 2Sb(s) + 6Si(s) + 3CaCl_2(s)$

**14.** $KI(aq) + HNO_3(aq) \rightarrow$
 $I_2(s) + KNO_3(aq) + NO(g) + H_2O(l)$

$$3(+1) = +3$$

$KI(aq) + HNO_3(aq) \rightarrow I_2(s) + KNO_3(aq) + NO(g) + H_2O(l)$

$$-3$$

$6KI(aq) + 8HNO_3(aq) \rightarrow$
 $3I_2(s) + 6KNO_3(aq) + 2NO(g) + 4H_2O(l)$

**15.** $Cr_2O_7{}^{2-}(aq) + SO_3{}^{2-}(aq) \rightarrow$
 $Cr^{3+}(aq) + SO_4{}^{2-}(aq)$ in an acidic solution

$$2(-3) = -6$$

$Cr_2O_7{}^{2-}(aq) + SO_3{}^{2-}(aq) \rightarrow Cr^{3+}(aq) + SO_4{}^{2-}(aq)$

$$3(+2) = +6$$

$Cr_2O_7{}^{2-}(aq) + 3SO_3{}^{2-}(aq) + 8H^+(aq) \rightarrow$
 $2Cr^{3+}(aq) + 3SO_4{}^{2-}(aq) + 4H_2O(l)$

**Write half-reactions for each of the following redox reactions. Identify each half-reaction as being either oxidation or reduction.**

**16.** $SnS_2(s) + O_2(g) \rightarrow SnO_2(s) + SO_2(g)$

$S^{2-} \rightarrow S^{4+} + 6e^-$, oxidation;
$O_2 + 4e^- \rightarrow 2O^{2-}$, reduction

**17.** $Mg(s) + N_2(g) \rightarrow Mg_3N_2(s)$

$Mg \rightarrow Mg^{2+} + 2e^-$, oxidation;
$N_2 + 6e^- \rightarrow 2N^{3-}$, reduction

**18.** $Al(s) + Cl_2(g) \rightarrow AlCl_3(s)$

$Al \rightarrow Al^{3+} + 3e^-$, oxidation;
$Cl_2 + 2e^- \rightarrow 2Cl^-$, reduction

**19.** $NH_3(aq) + PbO(s) \rightarrow$
 $N_2(g) + Pb(s) + H_2O(l)$

$2N^{3-} \rightarrow N_2 + 6e^-$, oxidation;
$Pb^{2+} + 2e^- \rightarrow 2Pb$, reduction

**20.** $Cu_2S(s) + O_2(g) \rightarrow Cu^{2+}(aq) + SO_4{}^{2-}(aq)$
(Hint: Two different elements are oxidized.)

$S^{2-} \rightarrow S^{4+} + 6e^-$, $Cu^+ \rightarrow Cu^{2+} + 1e^-$, oxidation;
$O_2 + 4e^- \rightarrow 2O^{2-}$, reduction

**Use your answers for questions 16–20 to help you balance the following equations, using half-reactions for the redox part of the equation. Show your work.**

**21.** $SnS_2(s) + O_2(g) \rightarrow SnO_2(s) + SO_2(g)$

$2(S^{2-} + S^{4+} + 6e^-)$; $3(O_2 + 4e^- \rightarrow 2O^{2-})$

$2S^{2-} \rightarrow + 2S^{4+} + 12e^-$
$3O_2 + 12e^- \rightarrow 6O^{2-}$

$SnS_2(s) + 3O_2(g) \rightarrow SnO_2(s) + 2SO_2(g)$

**22.** $Mg(s) + N_2(g) \rightarrow Mg_3N_2(s)$

$3(Mg \rightarrow Mg^{2+} + 2e^-); N_2 + 6e^- \rightarrow 2N^{3-}$

$3Mg \rightarrow 3Mg^{2+} + 6e^-$
$N_2 + 6e^- \rightarrow 2N^{3-}$

$3Mg(s) + N_2(g) \rightarrow Mg_3N_2(s)$

**23.** $Al(s) + Cl_2(g) \rightarrow AlCl_3(s)$

$2(Al \rightarrow Al^{3+} + 3e^-); 3(Cl_2 + 2e^- \rightarrow 2Cl^-)$

$2Al \rightarrow 2Al^{3+} + 6e^-$
$3Cl_2 + 6e^- \rightarrow 6Cl^-)$

$2Al(s) + 3Cl_2(g)\ 2AlCl_3(s)$

**24.** $NH_3(aq) + PbO(s) \rightarrow N_2(g) + Pb(s) + H_2O(l)$

$2N^{3-} \rightarrow N_2 + 6e^-; 3(Pb^{2+} + 2e^- \rightarrow 2Pb)$

$2N^{3-} \rightarrow N_2 + 6e^-$
$3Pb^{2+} + 6e^- \rightarrow 6Pb$

$2NH_3(aq) + 3PbO(s) \rightarrow N_2(g) + 3Pb(s) + 3H_2O(l)$

**25.** $Cu_2S(s) + O_2(g) \rightarrow Cu^{2+}(aq) + SO_4{}^{2-}(aq)$ in an acidic solution (Hint: Look at the ratio of the two oxidized elements in the equation.)

$Cu^+$ and $S^{2-}$ are both oxidized. According to the equation, two $Cu^+$ ions are oxidized for every one $S^{2-}$ ion oxidized, for a total loss of $10e^-$ for the oxidation part:

$S^{2-} \rightarrow S^{6+} + 8e^-$
$2Cu^+ \rightarrow 2Cu^{2+} + 2e^-$

reduction: $O_2 + 4e^- \rightarrow 2O^{2-}$

Because 20 is the least common multiple of 10 and 4, multiply the oxidation equations by 2 and the reduction equation by 5.

$2S^{2-} \rightarrow 2S^{6+} + 16e^-$
$4Cu^+ \rightarrow 4Cu^{2+} + 4e^-$
$5O_2 + 20e^- \rightarrow 10O^{2-}$

$2Cu_2S(s) + 5O_2(g) + 4H^+(aq) \rightarrow$
$\quad 4Cu^{2+}(aq) + 2SO_4{}^{2-}(aq) + 2H_2O(l)$

# Chapter 21

**Use data from Table 21-1 as needed in the following problems. Assume that all half-cells are under standard conditions.**

**1.** For each of these pairs of half-reactions, write a balanced equation for the overall cell reaction and calculate the standard cell potential, $E^0_{cell}$.

**a.** $Cs^+(aq) + e^- \rightarrow Cs(s)$
$Cu^+(aq) + e^- \rightarrow Cu(s)$

Cell reaction:

$Cu^+(aq) + Cs(s) \rightarrow Cu(s) + Cs^+(aq)$

$E^0_{cell} =$

$+0.521\ V - (-3.026\ V) = +3.547\ V$

**b.** $Hg^{2+}(aq) + 2e^- \rightarrow Hg(l)$
$Mn^{2+}(aq) + 2e^- \rightarrow Mn(s)$

Cell reaction:

$Hg^{2+}(aq) + Mn(s) \rightarrow Hg(l) + Mn^{2+}(aq)$

$E^0_{cell} =$

$+0.851\ V - (-1.185\ V) = +2.036\ V$

**c.** $Fe^{3+}(aq) + 3e^- \rightarrow Fe(s)$
$Cr^{3+}(aq) + 3e^- \rightarrow Cr(s)$

Cell reaction:

$Fe^{3+}(aq) + Cr(s) \rightarrow Fe(s) + Cr^{3+}(aq)$

$E^0_{cell} =$

$-0.037\ V - (-0.744\ V) = +0.707\ V$

**d.** $Br_2(g) + 2e^- \rightarrow 2Br^-(aq)$
$Au^+(aq) + e^- \rightarrow Au(s)$

Cell reaction:

$2Au^+(aq) + 2Br^-(aq) \rightarrow 2Au(s) + Br_2(g)$

$E^0_{cell} =$

+1.692 V − (+1.06 V) = +0.632 V; round to +0.63 V

**e.** $Be^{2+}(aq) + 2e^- \rightarrow Be(s)$

$Tl^{3+}(aq) + 3e^- \rightarrow Tl(s)$

Cell reaction:

$2Tl^{3+}(aq) + 3Be(s) \rightarrow 2Tl(s) + 3Be^{2+}(aq)$

$E^0_{cell} =$

+0.741 V − (−1.847 V) = +2.558 V

**f.** $NO_3^-(aq) + 4H^+(aq) + 3e^- \rightarrow$
$\quad NO(g) + 2H_2O(l)$

$In^{3+}(aq) + 3e^- \rightarrow In(s)$

Cell reaction:

$NO_3^-(aq) + 4H^+(aq) + In(s) \rightarrow$
$\quad NO(g) + 2H_2O(l) + In^{3+}(aq)$

$E^0_{cell} =$

+0.957 V − (−0.3382 V) = +1.2952 V; round to +1.295 V

**g.** $H_3PO_4(aq) + 2H^+(aq) + 2e^- \rightarrow$
$\quad H_3PO_3(aq) + H_2O(l)$

$SeO_4^{2-}(aq) + 4H^+(aq) + 2e^- \rightarrow$
$\quad H_2SeO_3(aq) + H_2O(l)$

Cell reaction:

$SeO_4^{2-}(aq) + 2H^+(aq) + H_3PO_3(aq) \rightarrow$
$\quad H_2SeO_3(aq) + H_3PO_4(aq)$

$E^0_{cell} =$

+1.151 V − (−0.276 V) = +1.427 V

**h.** $MnO_4^-(aq) + 8H^+(aq) + 5e^- \rightarrow$
$\quad Mn^{2+}(aq) + 4H_2O(l)$

$2CO_2(g) + 2H^+(aq) + 2e^- \rightarrow H_2C_2O_4(aq)$

Cell reaction:

$2MnO_4^-(aq) + 6H^+(aq) + 5H_2C_2O_4(aq) \rightarrow$
$\quad 2Mn^{2+}(aq) + 8H_2O(l) + 10CO_2(g)$

$E^0_{cell} =$

+1.507 V − (−0.49 V) = +1.997 V; round to +2.00 V

**2.** Calculate the standard cell potential, $E^0_{cell}$, for a cell composed of a $Sn|Sn^{2+}$ half-cell and each of these half-cells.

**a.** $Pd|Pd^{2+}$

$E^0_{cell} =$

+0.951 V − (−0.1375 V) = +1.0885 V; round to +1.089 V

**b.** $Hf|Hf^{4+}$

$E^0_{cell} =$

−0.1375 V − (−1.55 V) = +1.4125 V; round to +1.41 V

**c.** $Cl_2|Cl^-$

$E^0_{cell} =$

+1.35827 V − (−0.1375 V) = +1.49577 V; round to +1.4958 V

**d.** $Pb|Pb^{2+}$

$E^0_{cell} =$

−0.1262 V − (−0.1375 V) = +0.0113 V

**3.** Which of the following cells will produce the highest voltage?

$Mn|Mn^{2+}\|Zn^{2+}|Zn$

$Zn|Zn^{2+}\|Ni^{2+}|Ni$

$Ni|Ni^{2+}\|Cu^{2+}|Cu$

$E^0_{cell}$ (Mn-Zn) = $-0.7618$ V $- (-1.185$ V$)$ = $+0.4232$ V; round to $+0.423$ V

$E^0_{cell}$ (Zn-Ni) = $-0.257$ V $- (-0.7618$ V$)$ = $+0.5048$ V; round to $+0.505$ V

$E^0_{cell}$ (Ni-Cu) = $+0.3419$ V $- (-0.257$ V$)$ = $+0.5989$ V; round to $+0.599$ V

The $Ni|Ni^{2+}\|Cu^{2+}|Cu$ half-cell will produce the highest voltage.

**4.** For each of these overall cell reactions, write the oxidation and reduction half-reactions, calculate the standard cell potential, $E^0_{cell}$, and determine if the reaction is spontaneous or not.

**a.** $Fe^{3+}(aq) + Co^{2+}(aq) \rightarrow Fe^{2+}(aq) + Co^{3+}(aq)$

Oxidation half-reaction:

$Co^{2+}(aq) \rightarrow Co^{3+}(aq) + e^-$

Reduction half-reaction:

$Fe^{3+}(aq) + e^- \rightarrow Fe^{2+}(aq)$

$E^0_{cell} =$

$+0.771$ V $- (+1.92$ V$)$ = $-1.149$ V; round to $-1.15$ V

Spontaneous?

no

**b.** $Fe^{3+}(aq) + Cu^+(aq) \rightarrow Fe^{2+}(aq) + Cu^{2+}(aq)$

Oxidation half-reaction:

$Cu^+(aq) \rightarrow Cu^{2+}(aq) + e^-$

Reduction half-reaction:

$Fe^{3+}(aq) + e^- \rightarrow Fe^{2+}(aq)$

$E^0_{cell} =$

$+0.771$ V $- (+0.153$ V$)$ = $+0.618$ V

Spontaneous?

yes

**c.** $3Ni^{2+}(aq) + 2Rh(s) \rightarrow 3Ni(s) + 2Rh^{3+}(aq)$

Oxidation half-reaction:

$Rh(s) \rightarrow Rh^{3+}(aq) + 3e^-$

Reduction half-reaction:

$Ni^{2+}(aq) + 2e^- \rightarrow Ni(s)$

$E^0_{cell} =$

$-0.257$ V $- (+0.758$ V$)$ = $-1.015$ V

Spontaneous?

no

**d.** $2Na^+(aq) + 2Hg(l) + 2I^-(aq) \rightarrow 2Na(s) + Hg_2I_2(s)$

Oxidation half-reaction:

$2Hg(l) + 2I^-(aq) \rightarrow Hg_2I_2(s) + 2e^-$

Reduction half-reaction:

$Na+(aq) + e^- \rightarrow Na(s)$

$E^0_{cell} =$

$-2.71$ V $- (-0.0405$ V$)$ = $-2.6695$ V; round to $-2.67$ V

Spontaneous?

no

**e.** $O_2(g) + 2H_2SO_3(aq) \rightarrow$
$\quad 2SO_4^{2-}(aq) + 4H^+(aq)$

Oxidation half-reaction:

$H_2SO_3(aq) + H_2O(l) \rightarrow$
$\quad SO_4^{2-}(aq) + 4H^+(aq) + 2e^-$

Reduction half-reaction:

$O_2(g) + 4H^+(aq) + 4e^- \rightarrow 2H_2O(l)$

$E^0_{cell} =$

$+1.229 \text{ V} - (+0.172 \text{ V}) = +1.057 \text{ V}$

Spontaneous?

yes

**5.** Suppose a battery-powered device requires a minimum voltage of 9.0 V to run. How many lead–acid cells would be needed to run the device? (Remember that a standard automobile battery contains six lead–acid cells connected in one package.) The overall reaction of a lead–acid cell is

$Pb(s) + PbO_2(s) + 4H^+(aq) + 2SO_4^{2-}(aq)$
$\quad \rightarrow 2PbSO_4(s) + 2H_2O(l)$

$E^0_{cell} = +1.6913 \text{ V} - (-0.3588 \text{ V}) = +2.0501 \text{ V}$
$9.0 \text{ V}/2.0501 \text{ V} = 4.4$

At least 5 lead–acid cells would be needed to run the device.

**6.** What is the minimum voltage that must be applied to a Down's cell to cause the electrolysis of molten sodium chloride? The net cell reaction is

$2Na^+(l) + 2Cl^-(l) \rightarrow 2Na(l) + Cl_2(g)$
$E^0_{cell} = +1.35827 \text{ V} - (-2.71 \text{ V}) = +4.06827 \text{ V};$
round to $+4.07$ V

The minimum voltage to cause electrolysis is $-4.07$ V.

**7.** One way to determine the metallic composition of an alloy is to use electroplating. Suppose an electrolytic cell is set up with solution of nickel ions obtained from a 6.753-g sample of a nickel alloy. The cell also contains a platinum electrode that has a mass of 10.533 g. Electric current is used to reduce the nickel ions to nickel metal, which is deposited on the platinum electrode. After being plated with nickel, the platinum electrode has a mass of 15.042 g. What is the percentage of nickel in the alloy?

$$100\% \times \frac{(15.042 \text{ g} - 10.533 \text{ g})}{6.753 \text{ g}} = 66.77\%$$

# Chapter 22

**1.** Use the IUPAC rules to name the following alkanes.

**a.** $CH_3CH_2CH_2CH_2CH_3$

pentane

**b.**
$$\begin{array}{c} CH_3 \\ | \\ CH_3CHCHCH_3 \\ | \\ CH_3 \end{array}$$

2,3-dimethylbutane

**c.**
$$\begin{array}{c} CH_3 \quad CH_2CH_3 \\ | \qquad | \\ CH_3CH_2CHCHCHCH_2CH_3 \\ | \\ CH_2CH_3 \end{array}$$

3,4-diethyl-5-methylheptane

**d.**
$$\begin{array}{c} CH_3 \\ CH_3CH_2 \diagup \diagdown CH_2CH_3 \\ CH_3 \diagdown \diagup CH_3 \\ CH_2CH_3 \end{array}$$

1,3,5-triethyl-2,4,6-trimethylcyclohexane

**2.** Draw the structure of each of the following alkanes.

**a.** 4-propyloctane

$$CH_3CH_2CH_2\overset{\overset{\displaystyle CH_2CH_2CH_3}{|}}{C}HCH_2CH_2CH_2CH_3$$

**b.** 3,4-diethylhexane

$$CH_3CH_2\overset{\overset{\displaystyle CH_2CH_3}{|}}{C}H\underset{\underset{\displaystyle CH_2CH_3}{|}}{C}HCH_2CH_3$$

**c.** 2,2,4,4-tetramethylhexane

$$CH_3\overset{\overset{\displaystyle CH_3}{|}}{\underset{\underset{\displaystyle CH_3}{|}}{C}}CH_2\overset{\overset{\displaystyle CH_3}{|}}{\underset{\underset{\displaystyle CH_3}{|}}{C}}CH_2CH_3$$

**d.** 1-ethyl-3-methyl-2-propylcyclopentane

**3.** Calculate the number of hydrogen atoms in each of the following alkanes.

**a.** heptane

Straight-chain alkanes have the formula $C_nH_{2n+2}$. In heptane, $n = 7$, so the number of hydrogen atoms = $(2 \times 7) + 2 = 16$.

**b.** cyclooctane

Cyclic alkanes with one ring have the same number of hydrogen atoms as straight-chain alkanes, less two hydrogen atoms lost when the ring is formed. In cyclooctane, $n = 8$, so the number of hydrogen atoms = $(2 \times 8) + 2 - 2 = 16$.

**4.** Calculate the molecular mass of a 22-carbon branched-chain alkane.

Branched-chain alkanes have the formula $C_nH_{2n+2}$.

If $n = 22$, the number of hydrogen atoms = $(2 \times 22) + 2 = 46$.

| | | |
|---|---|---|
| 22 atoms C | $22 \times 12.011$ amu = | 264.24 amu |
| 46 atoms H | $46 \times 1.008$ amu = | 46.37 amu |
| molecular mass | | 310.61 amu |

**5.** Chemists can analyze the composition of hydrocarbons by reacting them with copper oxide. The reaction converts carbon into carbon dioxide and hydrogen into water. Suppose 29 g of a hydrocarbon reacts to produce 88 g of $CO_2$ and 45 g of $H_2O$.

**a.** What are the masses of carbon and hydrogen in the hydrocarbon?

All of the carbon in $CO_2$ and all of the hydrogen in $H_2O$ come from the hydrocarbon.

molecular mass $CO_2$ = $(1 \times 12.0$ amu) + $(2 \times 16.0$ amu) = 44.0 amu

mass C = 88 g $CO_2 \times$ (12 g C/44 g $CO_2$) = 24 g

molecular mass $H_2O$ = $(2 \times 1.0$ amu) + $(1 \times 16.0$ amu) = 18.0 amu

mass H = 45 g $H_2O \times$ (2.0 g C/18 g $H_2O$) = 5.0 g

**b.** What is the empirical formula of the hydrocarbon?

24 g C $\times$ (1 mole C/12 g C) = 2 moles C

5 g H $\times$ (1 mole H/1 g H) = 5 moles H

The empirical formula is $C_2H_5$.

**c.** If the hydrocarbon's molecular mass is 58 amu, what is its molecular formula?

The empirical formula ($C_2H_5$) corresponds to a molecular mass of $(2 \times 12$ amu) + $(5 \times 1$ amu) = 29 amu. Since $\dfrac{58 \text{ amu}}{29 \text{ amu}} = 2$, the molecular formula must be twice the empirical formula, or $C_4H_{10}$.

6. Carbon has an electronegativity of 2.5. Hydrogen has an electronegativity of 2.2. Use these values to decide whether each of the following bonds is polar or nonpolar.

   **a.** C-C

   2.5 − 2.5 = 0. Since the difference is less than 0.5, the bond is nonpolar.

   **b.** C-H

   2.5 − 2.2 = 0.3. Since the difference is less than 0.5, the bond is nonpolar.

   **c.** H-H

   2.2 − 2.2 = 0. Since the difference is less than 0.5, the bond is nonpolar.

7. The combustion of a saturated hydrocarbon releases 657 kJ per mole of –CH$_2$– groups and 779 kJ per mole of –CH$_3$ groups in the hydrocarbon. How much energy is released by the combustion of 1.00 L of liquid tetradecane (molecular formula C$_{14}$H$_{30}$), a major component of kerosene? The density of tetradecane is 0.764 g/mL.

   | 14 atoms C | 14 × 12.011 amu = | 168.15 amu |
   |---|---|---|
   | 30 atoms H | 30 × 1.008 amu = | 30.24 amu |
   | molecular mass | | 198.39 amu |

   1.00 L × (10$^3$ mL/1 L) × (0.764 g/mL) × (1 mole/198.39 g) = 3.85 moles tetradecane

   Each molecule of tetradecane has 12 –CH$_2$– groups and 2 –CH$_3$ groups.

   3.85 moles tetradecane × (12 moles –CH$_2$–/mole tetradecane) × (657 kJ/mole –CH$_2$–) = 30 400 kJ

   3.85 moles tetradecane × (2 moles –CH$_3$/mole tetradecane) × (779 kJ/mole –CH$_3$) = 6000 kJ

   30 400 kJ + 6000 kJ = 36 400 kJ = 3.64 × 10$^4$ J

8. Use the IUPAC rules to name the following hydrocarbons.

   **a.** CH$_3$CH$_2$CH=CHCH$_3$

   2-pentene

   **b.**
   CH=CH$_2$
   CH$_3$CH$_2$CH$_2$CHCH$_2$CH$_2$CH$_2$CH$_3$

   3-propyl-1-heptene

   **c.**
   CH$_3$
   CH$_3$CHCH$_2$CH$_2$C≡CH

   5-methyl-1-hexyne

   **d.** CH$_3$–⬡–CH$_2$CH$_3$

   1-ethyl-4-methylbenzene

9. Draw the structure of each of the following hydrocarbons.

   **a.** 7-methyl-2,5-nonadiene
   CH$_3$
   CH$_3$CH=CHCH$_2$CH=CHCHCH$_2$CH$_3$

   **b.** 4-ethyl-2-heptyne
   CH$_2$CH$_3$
   CH$_3$C≡CCHCH$_2$CH$_2$CH$_3$

   **c.** 1,2-diethylcyclohexene
   CH$_2$CH$_3$ / CH$_2$CH$_3$

   **d.** 1-ethyl-2-methyl-5-propylbenzene
   CH$_2$CH$_3$ CH$_3$ CH$_3$CH$_2$CH$_2$

**10.** Calculate the number of hydrogen atoms in each of the following unsaturated hydrocarbons.

**a.** 2-pentene

Alkenes with one double bond have the formula $C_nH_{2n}$. In 2-pentene, $n = 5$, so the number of hydrogen atoms = $2 \times 5 = 10$.

**b.** 1-hexyne

Alkynes with one triple bond have the formula $C_nH_{2n-2}$. In 1-hexyne, $n = 6$, so the number of hydrogen atoms = $(2 \times 6) - 2 = 10$.

**11.** Write a balanced equation for the reaction in which calcium carbide, $CaC_2$, reacts with water to form ethyne and calcium hydroxide.

$$CaC_2 + 2H_2O \rightarrow C_2H_2 + Ca(OH)_2$$

# Chapter 24

**1.** Calculate the molecular masses of the following biological molecules.

**a.** Lysine, $NH_2(CH_2)_4CHNH_2COOH$

| | | |
|---|---|---|
| 6 atoms C | $6 \times 12.0$ u = | 72.0 u |
| 14 atoms H | $14 \times 1.0$ u = | 14.0 u |
| 2 atoms O | $2 \times 16.0$ u = | 32.0 u |
| 2 atoms N | $2 \times 14.0$ u = | 28.0 u |
| molecular mass | | 146.0 u |

**b.** Fructose, $CH_2OHCO(CHOH)_3CH_2OH$

| | | |
|---|---|---|
| 6 atoms C | $6 \times 12.0$ u = | 72.0 u |
| 12 atoms H | $12 \times 1.0$ u = | 12.0 u |
| 6 atoms O | $6 \times 16.0$ u = | 96.0 u |
| molecular mass | | 180.0 u |

**c.** Oleic acid, $CH_3(CH_2)_7CH{=}CH(CH_2)_7COOH$

| | | |
|---|---|---|
| 18 atoms C | $18 \times 12.0$ u = | 216.0 u |
| 34 atoms H | $34 \times 1.0$ u = | 34.0 u |
| 2 atoms O | $2 \times 16.0$ u = | 32.0 u |
| molecular mass | | 282.0 u |

**2.** Write a balanced equation for the condensation reaction in which cysteine and glycine combine to form a dipeptide. Assume the carboxyl group of cysteine reacts.

**3.** In a peptide or protein that contains $n$ amino acids, the number of possible amino acid sequences is $A^n$, where $A$ is the number of different amino acids.

**a.** How many amino acid sequences are possible for a polypeptide that contains 10 amino acids?

$A = 20$, so the number of possible amino acid sequences = $20^{10} = 1.024 \times 10^{13}$.

**b.** How many different dipeptides can be made from the amino acids leucine (Leu) and valine (Val)? What are those dipeptides?

$A = 2$, so the number of different dipeptides = $2^2 = 4$. The dipeptides are Leu-Leu, Leu-Val, Val-Leu, and Val-Val.

4. Write a balanced equation for the condensation reaction in which lauric acid, palmitic acid, and stearic acid combine with glycerol to form a triglyceride.

$$CH_3(CH_2)_{10}COOH \qquad CH_3(CH_2)_{14}COOH$$
$$\text{lauric acid} \qquad\qquad \text{palmitic acid}$$
$$CH_3(CH_2)_{16}COOH$$
$$\text{stearic acid}$$

$$
\begin{array}{l}
CH_2OH \quad HO-\overset{\overset{O}{\|}}{C}(CH_2)_{10}CH_3 \qquad CH_2-O-\overset{\overset{O}{\|}}{C}(CH_2)_{10}CH_3\\[4pt]
\quad|\qquad\qquad \overset{\overset{O}{\|}}{\phantom{C}}\qquad\qquad\qquad | \qquad\qquad \overset{\overset{O}{\|}}{\phantom{C}}\\[2pt]
CHOH + HO-\overset{\overset{O}{\|}}{C}(CH_2)_{14}CH_3 \longrightarrow CH-O-\overset{\overset{O}{\|}}{C}(CH_2)_{14}CH_3 + 3H_2O\\[4pt]
\quad|\qquad\qquad \overset{\overset{O}{\|}}{\phantom{C}}\qquad\qquad\qquad | \qquad\qquad \overset{\overset{O}{\|}}{\phantom{C}}\\[2pt]
CH_2OH \quad HO-\overset{\overset{O}{\|}}{C}(CH_2)_{16}CH_3 \qquad CH_2-O-\overset{\overset{O}{\|}}{C}(CH_2)_{16}CH_3
\end{array}
$$

5. In saponification, the ester bonds of a triglyceride are hydrolyzed by a strong base, such as NaOH. It takes 3 moles of NaOH to saponify each mole of triglyceride. How many moles of triglyceride can be saponified by 120 g of NaOH?

$$(120 \text{ g NaOH})\left(\frac{1 \text{ mol NaOH}}{40 \text{ g NaOH}}\right)\left(\frac{1 \text{ mol triglyceride}}{3 \text{ mol NaOH}}\right)$$
$$= 1 \text{ mol triglyceride}$$

6. A young adult male produces about $2.4 \times 10^{-5}$ mol per day of the steroid sex hormone testosterone. The molecular mass of testosterone is 288. How many grams of testosterone per day does a young adult male produce?

$$\frac{(2.4 \times 10^{-5} \text{ mol testosterone})(288 \text{ g testosterone})}{1 \text{ mol testosterone}}$$
$$= 6.9 \times 10^{-3} \text{ g testosterone}$$

7. Synthesizing fats is an efficient way for organisms to store energy. The catabolism of 1 g of fat yields about 38 kJ of energy, whereas the catabolism of 1 g of protein or carbohydrate yields about 17 kJ of energy.

   a. How much carbohydrate would be needed to store the same amount of energy as 10 g of fat?

$$(10 \text{ g fat})\left(\frac{38 \text{ kJ}}{\text{g fat}}\right)\left(\frac{1 \text{ g carbohydrate}}{17 \text{ kJ}}\right)$$
$$= 22 \text{ g carbohydrate}$$

   b. A cup (133 g) of ice cream contains about 32 g of carbohydrate, 4.8 g of protein, and 14 g of fat. How much energy is released when a cup of ice cream is fully catabolized?

| | | |
|---|---|---|
| carbohydrate: | 32 g × 17 kJ/g = | 544 kJ |
| protein: | 4.8 g × 17 kJ/g = | 82 kJ |
| fat: | 14 g × 38 kJ/g = | 532 kJ |
| total: | | 1158 kJ |

$$(\text{about } 1.2 \times 10^6 \text{ J})$$

   c. A person expends about 840 kJ per hour while walking at a moderate pace. How long would a person have to walk to expend all of the energy contained in a cup of ice cream?

$$\frac{1158 \text{ kJ} \times 1 \text{ h}}{840 \text{ kJ}} = 1.4 \text{ h}$$

8. A scientist analyzes a sample of DNA and finds that 21% of the nucleotide bases are A and 29% of the bases are C. What percentage of the bases are T and what percentage are G in the sample?

   The amount of T always equals the amount of A, and the amount of G always equals the amount of C. Therefore, 21% of the nucleotide bases are T and 29% of the bases are G.

**9.** It takes three consecutive nucleotides in a DNA molecule to code for one amino acid in a protein. If a single strand of DNA contains 747 nucleotides, how many amino acids would be in the protein that it codes for?

$$\frac{(747 \text{ nucleotides})(1 \text{ amino acid})}{3 \text{ nucleotides}}$$

= 249 amino acids

**10.** The DNA in a bacterial cell contains about $4.2 \times 10^6$ complementary base pairs. Each base pair has an average length of $3.4 \times 10^{-10}$ m. How long is the DNA in a bacterial cell? Assume that the DNA is stretched out straight rather than coiled.

$$\frac{(4.2 \times 10^6 \text{ base pairs})(3.4 \times 10^{-10} \text{ m})}{\text{base pair}}$$

= $1.4 \times 10^{-3}$ m

**11.** One mole of ATP stores approximately 30.5 kJ of energy. This energy is released when ATP is hydrolyzed.

**a.** Approximately 38 moles of ATP is produced for each mole of glucose that is catabolized in cellular respiration. How much energy is stored in ATP when 5.0 moles of glucose is catabolized in cellular respiration?

$(5.0 \text{ mol glucose})\left(\dfrac{38 \text{ mol ATP}}{1 \text{ mol glucose}}\right)\left(\dfrac{30.5 \text{ kJ}}{1 \text{ mol ATP}}\right)$

= $5.8 \times 10^6$ J

**b.** Assume that 40% of this energy can be used to drive anabolic reactions when ATP is hydrolyzed. The rest will be lost as heat. How much energy will be lost as heat if all of the ATP produced in part a is hydrolyzed?

Total energy = energy used to drive anabolic reactions + energy lost as heat

100% = 40% + energy lost as heat

energy lost as heat = 100% − 40% = 60%

$5.8 \times 10^6$ J × 60% = $3.5 \times 10^6$ J

**12.** A scientist performed an experiment to monitor photosynthesis by a plant. In the experiment, the plant produced 61 g of glucose.

**a.** How many moles of glucose did the plant produce?

$$\frac{(61 \text{ g glucose})(1 \text{ mol glucose})}{180 \text{ g glucose}}$$

= 0.34 mol glucose

**b.** How many moles of $O_2$ did the plant produce?

$\dfrac{(0.34 \text{ mol glucose})(6 \text{ mol } O_2)}{1 \text{ mol glucose}}$ = 2.0 mol $O_2$

**c.** How many moles of $CO_2$ were needed to produce that much glucose?

$\dfrac{(0.34 \text{ mol glucose})(6 \text{ mol } CO_2)}{1 \text{ mol glucose}}$ = 2.0 mol $CO_2$

**d.** What mass of water was needed to produce that much glucose?

$(0.34 \text{ mol glu})\left(\dfrac{6 \text{ mol } H_2O}{1 \text{ mol glu}}\right)\left(\dfrac{18 \text{ g } H_2O}{1 \text{ mol } H_2O}\right)$

= 36 g $H_2O$

**13.** An average-sized woman produces about 1900 g of carbon dioxide per day.

**a.** How many moles of glucose must be oxidized during cellular respiration to produce that much carbon dioxide?

$(1900 \text{ g } CO_2)\left(\dfrac{1 \text{ mol } CO_2}{44 \text{ g } CO_2}\right)\left(\dfrac{1 \text{ mol glucose}}{6 \text{ mol } CO_2}\right)$

= 7.2 mol glucose

**b.** How much energy would be stored in ATP when that much glucose is oxidized?

$(7.2 \text{ mol glucose})\left(\dfrac{38 \text{ mol ATP}}{1 \text{ mol glucose}}\right)\left(\dfrac{30.5 \text{ kJ}}{1 \text{ mol ATP}}\right)$

= 8300 kJ (or $8.3 \times 10^6$ J)

**14.** Suppose the catabolism of a given amount of glucose produces 95 moles of ATP during cellular respiration. How many moles of ATP could be produced by the same amount of glucose during fermentation?

$$\frac{(95 \text{ mol ATP}_{CR})(2 \text{ mol ATP}_F)}{38 \text{ mol ATP}_{CR}} = 5.0 \text{ mol ATP}_F$$

**15.** How many grams of glucose are needed to produce 102 g of ethanol during alcoholic fermentation?

$$(102 \text{ g ethanol})\left(\frac{1 \text{ mol ethanol}}{46 \text{ g ethanol}}\right)\left(\frac{1 \text{ mol glucose}}{2 \text{ mol ethanol}}\right)$$
$$\left(\frac{180 \text{ g glucose}}{1 \text{ mol glucose}}\right) = 2.00 \times 10^2 \text{ g glucose}$$

**16.** Write a balanced equation for lactic acid fermentation. The formula for lactic acid is $CH_3CH(OH)COOH$.

$$C_6H_{12}O_6 \rightarrow 2CH_3CH(OH)COOH$$

# Chapter 25

**Write a complete nuclear equation for each of the following.**

**1.** The decay of $^{53}_{26}Fe$ by beta emission.

$$^{53}_{26}Fe \rightarrow {}^{0}_{-1}\beta + {}^{53}_{27}Co$$

**2.** The decay of $^{230}_{90}Th$ by alpha emission.

$$^{230}_{90}Th \rightarrow {}^{4}_{2}He + {}^{226}_{88}Ra$$

**3.** The decay of $^{37}_{18}Ar$ by electron capture.

$$^{37}_{18}Ar + {}^{0}_{-1}e \rightarrow {}^{37}_{17}Cl + X \text{ ray photon}$$

**4.** The decay of $^{38}_{19}K$ by positron emission.

$$^{38}_{19}K \rightarrow {}^{0}_{1}\beta + {}^{38}_{18}Ar$$

**5.** The decay of $^{93}_{43}Tc$ by gamma emission.

$$^{93}_{43}Tc \rightarrow {}^{0}_{0}\gamma + {}^{93}_{43}Tc$$

**Provide the missing term in each of the following equations.**

**6.** $^{11}_{5}B + {}^{4}_{2}He \rightarrow {}^{14}_{7}N + \underline{{}^{1}_{0}n}$

**7.** $^{45}_{20}Ca + {}^{1}_{1}p \rightarrow {}^{45}_{21}Sc + \underline{{}^{1}_{0}n}$

**8.** $^{15}_{7}N + \underline{{}^{4}_{2}He} \rightarrow {}^{18}_{8}O + {}^{1}_{1}p$

**9.** $^{233}_{92}U + {}^{1}_{0}n \rightarrow {}^{99}_{42}Mo + 3{}^{1}_{0}n + \underline{{}^{132}_{50}Sn}$

**10.** $\underline{{}^{210}_{84}Po} \rightarrow {}^{206}_{82}Pb + {}^{4}_{2}He$

**11.** $^{142}_{58}Ce + \underline{{}^{1}_{1}p} \rightarrow {}^{142}_{59}Pr + {}^{1}_{0}n$

**12.** $^{102}_{44}Ru + {}^{4}_{2}He \rightarrow {}^{1}_{0}n + \underline{{}^{105}_{46}Pd}$

**Answer the following questions about half-life.**

**13.** The half-life of $^{115}_{51}Sb$ is 32 minutes. How much of a 16.0-g sample of this isotope will remain at the end of 3.0 hours?

0.34 g $^{115}_{51}Sb$

Solution:

$$3 \text{ hours} \times \frac{60 \text{ minutes}}{1 \text{ hour}} = 180 \text{ minutes}$$

Amount remaining = Initial amount $(1/2)^{t/T}$

Amount remaining = 16.0 g $\times (1/2)^{\frac{180 \text{ minutes}}{32 \text{ minutes}}}$

Amount remaining = 16.0 g $\times (1/2)^{5.6}$

Amount remaining = 16.0 g $\times 0.021 = 0.34$ g

**14.** The half-life of $^{182}_{72}$Hf is $9.0 \times 10^6$ years. How much of a 1.0-g sample of this isotope will remain at the end of 40.0 million years?

0.047 g $^{182}_{72}$Hf

**Solution:**

40 million years = $4.0 \times 10^7$ years

Amount remaining = Initial amount $(1/2)^{t/T}$

Amount remaining = 1.0 g $\times$ $(1/2)^{\frac{4.0 \times 10^7 \, \cancel{yr}}{9.0 \times 10^6 \, \cancel{yr}}}$

Amount remaining = 1.0 g $\times$ $(1/2)^{4.4}$

Amount remaining = 1.0 g $\times$ 0.047 = 0.047 g

**15.** The isotope strontium-90 is produced during the testing of nuclear weapons. If 100.0 mg of strontium-90 was released in the atmosphere in 1960, how much of the radioisotope remains 85 years later? The half life of strontium-90 is 29 years.

13 mg strontium-90

**Solution:**

Amount remaining = Initial amount $(1/2)^{t/T}$

Amount remaining = 100.0 mg $\times$ $(1/2)^{\frac{85 \, \cancel{years}}{29 \, \cancel{years}}}$

Amount remaining = 100.0 mg $\times$ $(1/2)^{2.9}$

Amount remaining = 100.0 mg $\times$ 0.13 = 13 mg

**16.** The radioisotope technetium-99 is often used as a radiotracer to detect disorders of the body. It has a half-life of 6.01 hours. If a patient received a 25.0-mg dose of this isotope during a medical procedure, how much would remain 48.0 hours after the dose was given?

1.05 mg technetium-99

**Solution:**

Amount remaining = Initial amount $(1/2)^{t/T}$

Amount remaining = 25.0 mg $\times$ $(1/2)^{\frac{48.0 \, \cancel{hours}}{6.01 \, \cancel{hours}}}$

Amount remaining = 25.0 mg $\times$ $(1/2)^{7.99}$

Amount remaining = 25.0 mg $\times$ 0.00419

Amount remaining = 1.05 mg